# One Man's Opinion

D1270694

**Reinaldo Irizarry, Sr., Ph.D.**

A series of articles contributed by the Author expressing scenarios depicting possible factual, Fictional, Educational, Philosophical, Instructional, Science, and a touch of sensitivity:

You be the Judge...

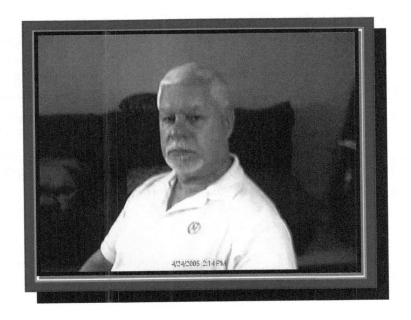

# Dedication

**"This book is dedicated to my lovely Wife, Ellie, with all my love, who has supported me and has given me encouragement and inspiration."**

## Thoughts to ponder.

*Love your neighbor as you love God! Think positive, stay focused on everything you do throughout your life and try to help everyone you meet along the way. Be the best that you can be at anything you put your mind to, which will serve as an example for others to follow. Be a Mentor, a brother, but most of all, a friend. Be compassionate, trustworthy, loyal, understanding, faithful, and a good listener, and you will have the world at your feet alongside the side of GOD. Keep an open mind to all good possibilities that may affect your life, your family, and your friends. Stay positive, my friend, and you will have the blessing of the Universe and all its wonder.*

# TABLE OF CONTENT

# Bombs over the USA

Since Israel became a state in 1948, it has been on guard against invaders from all sides, in been surrounded by lifelong enemies seeking its destruction. The country, which is small, is always seeking stable and peaceful relations with its neighbor in the area. For over Sixty years, Israel, with belief in peaceful co-existence, has been waging a losing battle with its neighbors to stop their aggression, a long time for a country to be concerned about its well-being, security, and survival.

During the first war in 1991 between the US and Iraq, they endured Scuds missile bombing attacks from Saddam Hussein against their homeland. They suffered destruction losing many lives. It is difficult to stand by idle while receiving missiles over your head, knowing they are killing your people, and not be able to retaliate because you are asked not to do so. You would think a country so small, being under so much pressure for so long, would be used to it by now. I cannot begin to imagine the frightening experience everyone goes through every day living in that country. Yet they go on with their everyday lives with striving and perseverance

Israel has shown and exercised self-restraint more than any other country in the region. Showing the rest of the World they could endure hardship and misery just as they had done during World War

II and centuries before. Still, be victorious by not retaliating when the US asked not to during the war with Iraq. It takes great people and a great Nation to be well discipline-exercising self-restraint in moments of great personal danger and misfortune. The confusion they face while getting up every morning and going on with their daily routine in trying to live a healthy life must be horrendous.

When Saddam Hussein started to expand his philosophy of tyranny after the Iraq, Iran War, it would have been but a matter before he attacked Israel, causing an incident more disastrous than he could have imagined. Much greater than when he invaded Kuwait. The cruel and deadly treatment he exercised against his own people while he was the Dictator is on record for all to read.

He proved to have had weapons of mass destruction when he used poisonous gas, killing thousands of people in the Northern Part of Iraq. There are rumors that he used it against Iranian soldiers during his conflict with Iran. When realizing the United States would finally be on his doorstep, he had no other choice but to have them transported to Syria. He had them placed in underground bunkers somewhere in the desert. One of his former Generals who knew and was aware of their locations revealed this information to the public and to the US. It would have only been a matter of time before Saddam Hussein would have expanded his power by further using them against Israel and becoming a menace in the entire area.

# ONE MAN'S OPINION

In miscalculating his political actions and creating bad relations with the US, Saddam Hussein brought on his own destruction and that of his country. However, the real threat was not Iraq but Iran; they are the ones causing all the problems in the region; they were doing it before; they are doing it now. They are the ones responsible for all turmoil in the area. They are the ones who are training all the outside fighters who are coming into Iraq to kill our soldiers. They are the ones that want to see Israel wiped off from the face of the Earth with the good old USA. If left unchecked, Iran would eventually run over the Middle East and, in time, challenge the USA in a Nuclear War: They will first strike Israel with nuclear weapons and use it as an excuse to fight against the USA. They are fanatics who believe that their way is the only way. They know we will not hesitate to come to the aid of Israel, and that is what they are seeking, the end to civilization as we know it.

Iran is the Country everyone should be concerned with because they have a fanatical and crazy agenda behind their religious beliefs. They believe they have nothing to lose and everything to gain. Their main objective is turning the Middle East into a ball of fire or a burning inferno. They believe by killing themselves and taking as much of the so call infidels with them; they will reach heaven and have sixty virgins waiting for them. How sad to know there are people with such low-level of intelligence who believe such nonsense and false expectation:

Now it looks as if they may have the ability and the means to do it. The more they keep talking, the more they keep stalling. Allowing them more time in which they can complete building the bomb. Once they have it, they will use it. These people do not discriminate between races; they offer equal opportunity to erase everyone on this planet with their nuclear bomb. They will use them; there is no doubt about it…

In addition, if that were not bad enough, you have Mr. Chavez, from Venezuela and Castro, from Cuba, joining forces with this nut from Iran in this search for Islamic Utopia.

I call on the people of the United States, Citizens of the World, wake up… wake up… wake up. Our government should be at its highest alert stage, which is (RED). An ounce of prevention could well mean our survival. We must not allow it to happen. Not to Israel, not to any other country and certainly not the good old USA.

We must not allow ourselves to be taken by surprise with our pants down when the bombs are flying overhead. We must stop them now because later, it will be too late. It must be a joint effort between various countries, not just the great USA.

# Sloppy Joes in Police Work

What is it that makes young man women, when they graduate from the Police Academy, forget the basics involving police work? Instead, they develop a sense of being "Sloppy Joes." For some unknown reason, they discard all the training they have received insensitivity in dealing with the public.

The majority are right out of High school, have no life experience, and have limited education, with many only two years of college. Others are on a career move and just need a job. Others seek the opportunity to get a job with the potential to use for the wrong reasons: When the average citizen becomes a criminal, they are amateur. However, when a police officer goes outside the law and becomes a criminal, then you have good reasons to worry.

I was at the Academy when they advised and stressed strongly to all Police Recruits to be respectable and polite to the public and watch their language while not taking the job personally. I can assure you, throughout my twenty-Six-year career as a Police Officer, I followed that advice and still successfully performed my duties as described by the Constitution of the United States. To safeguard the rights of all persons regardless of their ethnic background or religious beliefs.

In today's world, events are happening fast. Everyone is in a hurry and not knowing where they are heading. Police Officers and members of Law Enforcement know well what modern technology has done to affect police work. It is a thankless task. Not understood by the average person; In addition, they are hated by criminals. However, as police officers, we must never lose touch with the actions we take because there will be an equal and opposite reaction, which will later affect our lives. In addition, regardless of who we are, we are accountable for our actions.

The average Police Department can hold fast to its well-established reputation that most of their Police Officers when they retire, do so with honor. However, because of their greed for power, unscrupulous individuals join the police force for personal gain, causing other good and faithful, devoted officers to suffer. Those who chose the profession with the best intent soon realize others who want to profit from the power that it brings them makes a black stigma on the profession.

Since my retirement from the force, I have had several instances where Officers have stopped me for no apparent purpose. When stopped, I asked why, and they just looked at me without a response walking away back to their Police vehicle. After ten minutes, they returned with my credentials and my license and, without giving me an answer, got back into their patrol car and drove away. I have had many of these unpleasant experiences with young Police Officers, both men and women.

The men, while talking to me, have been rude and disrespectful with their remarks. Showing me little regards, knowing I was a retired Officer. The women, on the other hand, are more understanding; however, they have displayed to be just as rude, lacking consideration while projecting a real macho image.

I can recall the many times I stopped a motorist for traffic violations. I always kept in mind I never knew whom I was stopping. Regardless of who it was, I would show respect and listen to what they had to say. This method gave me satisfactory results, and the experiences I gained gave me confidence which caused me to perfect my way of dealing with the public. It also taught me people skills, which are essential today. Whenever I stopped family members of Police Officers, I always upheld the highest Ethical standard to be fair and just and to exercise sound judgment in extending departmental professional courtesy.

There is something wrong with this picture, which needs addressing by all Police departments throughout this country to reduce the resentment of the public towards our Police Officers. I am sure these events occurred throughout the Country, involving other officers and citizens.

Police Officers must realize the responsibility they hold is an important one, and any action on their part reflects on the department they represent. The job requires well and sensible people with good judgment in handle ling the public. They must be truthful, honest, and fair to everyone. They will never know when they may be a victim of an incident and be a force in being straightforward with the facts and the truth.

Now I am saddened because of the way Police Officers today treat people on the streets. Especially when an Officer stops another Officer, the lack of respect and courtesy shown:

I have seen officers talk to motorists projecting an image of higher superiority when speaking to them. Showing no respect or attention to Senior Citizens reminding them of their own parents. When I see this, I get a bad taste in my mouth, and it saddens my heart because I wonder where they are getting these people.

Recently I had an unpleasant experience in having a Police Officer give my youngest son a summons without probable cause. It happened around SW 27th Avenue and Bird Road, Florida. My Son had just finished taking his little four (4) years old Son, my grandson, to the movies. He was on his way to buy his son a pizza at a shop owned by his friend in the city. The Officer stopped my son, claiming he was driving a 2004 Black Acura with a completely tinted front windshield. My Son was driving my car, which does not have a full front tinted windshield.

After carefully checking the tint "VLT" Visible Light Transmission reading of 70% and seeing it complied with state laws, the summons is invalid. The Officer, who issued the summons, failed to follow proper protocol in issuing the summons and displayed his lack of experience as a Police Officer. If he had used just a little common sense, he would have exercised good judgment in calling a supervisor to the scene with a meter. If he had taken a few minutes in using proper techniques, he would have found the front windshield in my car met Florida's DOT windshield "VLT" 70% tint specifications. He issued the Summons without using a meter and getting a proper reading. He did it by looking at the windshield, which is unacceptable and sloppy Police work.

When I bought the car, it was with factory specification, which complied with all standards met by the state of Florida DOT Visible Light Transmission guidelines, which is 70%. In other words, he issued a summons without probable cause.

This was not an isolated case. This often happens by several Officers looking for shortcuts when issuing summonses. When a Police Officer issues a summons for tinted front windshields, a calibrated meter is to be used to secure the motorist is in direct violation of the state's prescribed laws, showing the summons to be valid. Anything other is unacceptable.

The same applies when issuing a speeding ticket. All proper documentation dealing with the ticket must be present in Traffic Court, Including the Officer and the offender receiving the ticket.

The Officers must have in his possession while, in court, a copy of the violation given describing the total number of miles traveled over the posted speed limit in the area, all documentation about the Radar Gun used, the certificate showing the recent date of calibration and his citation log needed by his area.

These amazingly simple procedures, when correctly followed, will always win your case. Deviation from these procedures always makes an Officer lose his day in court and eventually lose faith in the Judge handling his case.

When Officers go out of their way to do sloppy Police work, it reflects on their agency, suggesting the lack of training, which they have not received. Causing more harm than good.

Therefore, I cannot understand why some Officers fall through the cracks and do the opposite of what they have learned. To avert some of these inconsistencies, Supervisors should stay on top of their officers and check on their performance.

Being a Police Officer gives you the capacity to learn how to think the same way as the criminal to defeat them at their game. Therefore, having an officer go bad and turn into a criminal is a serious matter. As a professional and now a retired Police officer, I do not relish the idea of having to face an ex-cop who has become a bad guy during a criminal confrontation. Which usually turns into a major crisis?

# ONE MAN'S OPINION

If the Police role is to be more of a profession like other professions, you must raise the standards and qualifications to be in pace and meet modern times. There must be better screening techniques to weed out the undesirable from the ranks. As it is now, a vast number of undesirable Police Officers have fallen through the cracks winding up in positions of a high level of authority and abusing their authority.

FYI:

Automobile window tinting, by its nature, reduces the visible light transmittance through a vehicle's windows. This can be problematic at night when motorists must be able to see through the windows of other cars to spot hazards. Police officers must also be able to identify the passengers in a vehicle.

In many jurisdictions, there are government rules in place to ensure darkness levels of films do not present a danger to motorists. To get the best results, it is also significant for Police Officers to use properly calibrated meters when taking readings.

In the United States, the federal Department of Transport specifies a minimum of 70% visible light transmission (VLT) for window tinting on the front windshield and the windows to the immediate left and right of the driver's side. The Dot does not specify any VLT must for any other windows. Individual states can pass laws that go further in the specifications set forth by the Dot. Private cars may have tints on the windows to the immediate left and right of the driver as dark as 20% VLT, depending on the situation.

The question which comes to mind is why Police Officers would risk making fools of themselves in the Court of Law by using sloppy techniques which will get them in trouble with Judges. Yet these incidents continue to take place in our traffic courts throughout this country.

Many Police Officers, instead of using common sense in doing what is right, are growing "Sloppy Joes," developing a credibility gap while in court with many Judges. It takes a joint effort by all of us to expose these bad apples to correct the problem.

# Guilty Until Proven Otherwise

I admired young men and women who put on a Police Uniform after graduating from the Police Academy and go out, putting their lives on the line to protect us. Furthermore, face unexpected and unforeseen danger lurking around every corner. However, usually, without proper training in sensitivity matters about different ethnic groups, diverse cultures, and people skills, the task becomes difficult.

Throughout history, the police have been viewed as "Pillars of Society." They held society together. The police provided the safety margin, "The Blue Safety Line," which keeps society from reaching anarchy.

The United States of America Constitution guarantees every American citizen equal rights. It describes precisely every person born in this country, and those sworn American citizens may enjoy the power of freedom. They have the right to pursue their dreams of worship, free from oppression and false accusations. They have the right to choose to petition the government for a redress of their grievances. They have the power of choice to voice their opinion on matters about the state in their Homeland. No other country in this world guarantees these rights.

In doing so, everyone takes advantage, and as a result, individual rights are abused. Creating different standards within society, which affect the citizens causing great discontent and unrest, often resulting in national civil disorder.

We live in a society where the criteria for the wealthy are different from those of the poor. However, what is most intriguing is that we have standards for the people that are responsible for our protection. The people that serve as our protectors throughout our homeland, our Police forces whose duty is to guard our freedom and keep us safe from harm's way, and from the criminal predators that prey on our citizens.

When it comes to equal justice, Law Enforcement personnel are placed in a separate category, therefore, seen differently. The average citizens are ignorant of most of the laws of our land. However, when it comes to people who know the law, the rules change. In other words, they should know better…

Most Police officers are young and just out of High School; some have college degrees, though; they still need life experience, which would cause them to be more skillful when communicating with the public. Police Officers subject themselves to people in communities that are much older and much more educated than they are.

One idea that should come to everyone's mind that would motivate and create a person is seeking a profession that could lead to the taking of human life or losing his Owen. It is a known fact that Police Officers have the supreme power to deprive anyone of his or her freedom. When a criminal commits a crime, they bring them in front of a judge to answer for the offense. Judges have a separate set of rules that they follow which is different from the ones when they have trained law enforcement personnel in front of them.

Communities expect Police Officers to be better educated as well as occasionally detain members of the community for various involvements in violation of the law. The public shows resentment toward these actions, and it creates a problem. It is not the Officers fault; it is just the way it is.

The expectation that the public has about our Police Officers is that when they respond to an incident, they should know precisely what to do. However, there are circumstances leading them to make mistakes during the call they may be involved, which becomes a legal problem. As a result, some may face disciplinary actions because the failure to follow proper procedures gets them into trouble.

When these officers are charged with violations of the law, they do not receive the same consideration or treatment as the average citizen. If an officer of the law commits a crime and subsequently goes to prison, he is isolated from the central prison population for security reasons. This alone should alert everyone that standards applying to Police Officers are different.

There is a public view about Police Officers that when they commit a crime, they are guilty until proven innocent. When it should be the other way around, in preventing these officers from suffering mental anguish, developing a sense of guilt, and eventually becoming dissolution with the job:

This does not happen to the average everyday criminal. They have ignored what the public thinks. The average person, who has experienced imprisonment many times, knows well how to get by while in confinement for extended periods. They have plenty of time while seating in prison to brush up on all kinds of skills, becoming nickel and dime lawyers while filing grievances and spending the taxpayer's money in seeking retrials for their offenses.

In some situations become even better Attorneys than the ones that represented them. These facts are the reasons our criminal justice concept is in such a shamble. There is a large number of law Enforcement Officers restricted to our Correctional Institutions that know their lives are in great danger. The people who are caring for them do not concern themselves with their safety because they know the shamble the whole concept finds itself.

Our nation is overburdened with crowded jails where inmates are placed four to a cell because they do not have enough room where to put them. In addition, executive bureaucrats responsible for the decisions on equal personnel distribution to maintain a balance are not doing their job.

In addition, mammy inmates confined in a limited space become irritated and frustrated; as a result, you have disturbances and riots. Knowing these causes, those who can make changes in developing new laws that will bring this to pass are only concerned about how much salary increase they can get the next time around.

Many officers imprisoned today are there because they failed to follow the law. Often using their Police authority for all the wrong reasons caused them to get into trouble, and they subsequently went to prison, bringing a stigma on the rest of the officers who must continue the war on crime; however, there are many officers in prison who should not be there. Somehow, they slipped through the cracks or, conveniently, no one noticed.

According to Article 7 of the "Bill of Rights," No one will be accountable or answer for a crime without sufficient data and an inquiry and formal accusation by a "Grand Jury." The Courts describe that anyone accused is "Innocent until Proven Guilty." Alternatively, is he?

When the average citizen commits a crime, they are innocent until proven guilty. However, when Police Officer faces the same circumstances, they are guilty until proven innocent. Having officers suspended without pay and bringing hardship to the officer and their families.

Whenever there is an internal investigation involving a Police Officer, their lives are placed on hold. Suspension can last for years until the final determination of their case. Often having their families turn their backs on them in fear of reprisal from the rest of the World rather than stand with them.

Further, they are seen as an outcast and not trusted by citizens in their community. Examined by the media causing many to feel robbed of their honor and integrity, forcing many to commit suicide rather than face disgraced. Anyone who thinks that police work is just as you see in the movies has another thin coming.

# The Lonely Unfortunate Ones

This is the part of society that no one wants to notice because it is a dark stigma to our way of life: Simply put, the homeless problem is a reality staring at us in our faces every day. Little do we understand for most people in our society are only a paycheck away from being homeless. Only wealthy individuals have the luxury and privilege of not having to be concerned with this problem.

However, they can also fall into the same quagmire and never recoup.

This is a problem incredibly old itself. Only recently have people begun to recognize and open their eyes to the ever-growing problem we encounter daily: living beyond our means. Overspending and not maintaining a reliable budget. If continued at the present trend, many people are going to find themselves in severe financial difficulty. Obviously, for many people, soon, the old prophecy is going to become a reality. The meek, the weak, and the homeless will inherit the Earth.

It is obvious; life gets harder for many people as time marches on. Many members of the workforce worked and set in twenty to thirty years in a job only to find their retirement pensions are not sufficient to meet their needs. As a result, returning to the workforce to meet their needs. This trend is becoming more acceptable today as the generations are getting older and people are living longer

I can remember when my father would tell me about the day he would retire. In addition, what he had planned to enjoy with the free time he would have. When retirement finally came, he discovered it was not the way he thought it would be. He found himself doing odd jobs just to keep food on the table. He found himself more stressed out than ever before. While my mother looked on with dismay and confusion about what the future held for them... He was facing the fact that most people, when retired, do not even think.

Seeing what was facing them, I would always tell them, "Dad, Mom, as long as I am alive, you both would never have to worry about not having enough food on the kitchen table." They would turn their heads to look at each other, turn back, and look at me with a pleasing look on their faces. That is how it was when my father and Mother were alive.

They are both gone now, but I am still reminiscent of those times. That experience taught me how to plan for the times ahead.

Months before my retirement, I had paid most of my bills so I would not find myself behind the eight-ball playing catch up. I did not want to find myself in a hole that most people find themselves in when they do retire. However, regardless of the preparation, you make to prevent it from happening, it always falls short, subsequently putting you right back the way you were before you started. For simple working people, this is the economic situation they tend to find themselves in, which does not seem to have an end. Regardless of how much money you make, it never is enough to cover new expenses you gain as you get older.

As I go around the country and do surveys on the topic, I have found most people are aware of the problem but need the incentive to act on it. As a result, the problem becomes an endless one with no ending in sight. It is a problem that has no importance until it hits home. Only then are they willing to put more effort into trying to find a solution.

Homeless people come from all occupations. There is no specific area to put the blame on. The majority find themselves in this condition because of economic events in their lives that have placed them there. In addition, there are many who have a history of mental problems.

Most homeless people I have spoken with look and function as average ordinary people. Only after having talked and probed into their private lives do you find the hidden causes behind their economic conditions.

As a Police Officer throughout my twenty-six-year career, I have had the experience of meeting people from all over society. Regardless of the many homeless community services we may have, there will never be enough to stop the homeless problem.

During my career, I can recall the many instances where I would meet homeless people and, after talking briefly with them, I would walk away with a different opinion of them. I took the opportunity to listen and watch while they were speaking and analyzing the words that they used. I found that many of them were educated and from solid family backgrounds.

Many were single individuals; others were entire families huddled together, keeping themselves warm during the winter. At times, I felt hopeless because I could not do enough to end their difficulty and their suffering. Many times, I would go home at the end of my shift, spending the rest of the time at home telling my wife what I had experienced, looking for her encouragement and understating to make me feel better.

Every day I take to heart that whenever I see homeless people, I try to help them in some way because you never know what your future holds. Whether we like it or not, we are our brother's keeper… In addition, in fact, it is not such a significant load on us to extend a helping hand.

# The Modern Gladiators

# The Neighborhood Resource Officers – NROs

This article will serve as a tribute to the modern, well-trained educated Gladiators known as the (NROs), Neighborhood Resource Officers. These modern warriors of young men and women have received a partner in the war against crime. This new partner is the community that they serve and help to protect.

This progressive approach, which has been around for many years, will help remove some of the barriers and stigma associated with police work existing between the Police and their communities across this land.

Today, as new laws come into effect, the emphasis is on community policing. As a result, most communities have a greater knowledge of the duties of police personnel during the performance of their duties. Besides, we have a higher number of educated citizens than ever before.

Because of personnel safety concerns, more communities are becoming more aggressive and are willing to take an active role in joining the police in combating crime. This partnership has also caused a change in the attitude of the community towards their police agencies.

Community leaders, and average citizens, are finally

realizing that ninety-five percent (95%) of police work involves prevention, helping citizens in need, promotion of law and order, and providing emergency services to the community.

The other five percent (5%) is the heartbreaking, wrenching involvement in vital police roles, such as search and seizure, arresting and imprisoning criminals.

An understanding by police personnel of their responsible role in police work is necessary to perform and help gain job satisfaction. Departmental training provides the means and methods through which police officers achieve their proper function perspective. Most significantly, it firmly shows that assistance to all citizens in need has become a service that all community citizens have come to expect and rely on from their police officers. Anything otherwise is unacceptable to the community.

This expectation from citizens in the community is so deeply rooted as the expectation that all police officers will safeguard all life and property. The overall effectiveness of police officers as individuals should always be encouraged by their competency, but also by their integrity and honor in providing all the necessary services to the community by police enforcement techniques which is respectful of individuals' rights.

Their effectiveness should never be compared to old, outdated traditional departmental police policies. The former compulsory departmental quota, which some police departments still enforce, is unacceptable and should be abolished.

The U.S. Attorney General and the Department of Justice should stress to all police agencies to stop these practices, which cause unnecessary stress on Police officers that are out on the streets, doing safe and efficient work.

Emphasis should be required in addressing the problem, which helps breed crime in communities. A joint effort and full cooperation between the police and the community must take place for this great venture to become a success.

It is obvious to everyone; the proper role and responsibility of any modern police officer are to protect and serve. The truth is most police officers go beyond the call of duty, and the community has complete disregard resulting in the loss of an officer's life.

Today's young men and women, who put on the Police uniform, do so because they believe they can make a difference. They believe just maybe that they may make our world a little bit safer. It is a fact, today, officers that are educated, with more life experience, view the profession as an honorable one. They come from all lifestyles, colors, and creeds and are more sensitive to the public's needs than past older police officers.

These qualities help show the communities the high degree of professionalism that exists today in police agencies throughout the country. The old practice of old hard-liner methods of going into a neighborhood by force, taking names, and kicking ass are no longer acceptable. The harsh and overzealous police officer who threatens or violates the rights of individual citizens and helps alienate the population in the community against its police is no longer acceptable.

With these facts, police officers or other members of any law enforcement agency, while performing their duties, should keep an awareness of the critical scrutiny received by the media and the community. Keeping in mind that all eyes are upon you whether you see them or not. Remembering honor and integrity is an important reason to consider before becoming a Police Officer because you must answer to yourself...

Learning to accept criticism, regardless of where it is coming from, whether it is positive or negative, and not overreacting is an important part of the job. We should all make a strong effort, take pride in our chosen profession to improve, and ensure professionalism in law enforcement continues. Putting on a police officer's uniform with a badge is the highest honor any person can ever hope to achieve.

A point to think about honor to God and Country; beyond the call of duty, we should take pride in our chosen profession and help develop and ensure professionalism in the criminal justice.

# ONE MAN'S OPINION

Duties of a true Police professional:

- Honor and loyalty to my chosen profession
- Assist citizens who cannot care for themselves due to their state of health, age, and disabilities
- Aid and protect anyone from danger or physical harm.
- Take immediate lifesaving actions in helping to move cars and people in an emergency or disaster.
- Reduce the opportunity for crime and misconduct through alert, aggressive patrol techniques in keeping with departmental guidelines and frequent vigilance.
- Identify, and prevent any criminal act, and when proper, arrest violators.
- Issue citations based on the violation of state statutes to violators when necessary.
- Identify, correct, and report any danger quickly.
- Assist and provide emergency services to other law enforcement agencies when needed.
- Extend information, direction, and courtesy to tourists visiting our city.

# Sample Narrative of a Violent Domestic Incident Police Report

On July 10, 2005, at 9:00 PM, I, Officer John Doe, was sent to a Violent Domestic call at 125 NW 111 Street Apt. #4A, South Point, Florida. On arrival, I met the (victim) White Female, _____ _____, DOB, 02/07/1960. She was crying and had five large cuts on the right side of her face and was bleeding. I immediately requested rescue and an ID-Unit to respond for photos of the Victims injuries.

While waiting for rescue, I asked what had happened, if there were any witnesses, and how long ago had it occurred. She said that it had just happened ten minutes before I had arrived. She said her husband White Male, _____ _____, DOB, 06/19/1955, had come home drunk. While noticing she did not have; his food ready began to hit her on her face with his right fist, causing several open cuts to her face. She said there were no witnesses. I immediately asked for a description and placed a BE ON THE LOOK OUT (BOLO) on all units in the immediate area.

She described her husband as a white male six feet tall, weighing about two hundred pounds, with a black mustache and short black hair. He had a two-inch scar on the right cheek of his face. He had on a long sleeve white shirt and faded blue jeans. He was driving a 2006 black four 4-door Chevy sedan with dark tinted windows with minor damage to the right front passenger door; it had Florida tag #000000. He left west on 111 Street and then turned North on 2 Avenue.

Rescue Unit #25 arrived, Lieutenant. Doe checked and treated the victim. He noticed her injuries needed medical attention. He asked if she would go with them to the hospital; however, she refused. He further advised her to seek medical attention as soon as possible before her injuries became infected. She agreed. ID Unit C-10 also arrived and took ten (10) photos of the victim's injuries.

I advised the victim on the procedure to follow involving a Violent Domestic Victim and how to seek a restraining order against her husband for protection. I gave her a Domestic Victims Pamphlet describing all the necessary steps with all the phone numbers she needed. I then called and placed her in contact with a Victims Domestic Violent Advocate for further counseling. I then left and canvassed the area for the defendant and notified the dispatcher with negative results.

Detective John Smith, Unit-109 from the Violent Domestic section, was notified of the incident, and I sent him a copy of the report for further investigation, follow-up, and final disposition of the case.

# This Desert called Earth

We have about a good (two hundred) years before our planet; "Earth" becomes a waist land, one of the many deserts in the Universe. We have the resources, but we lack the most important reason, the willpower how to prevent it from happening. Wrapping ourselves with other unimportant matters is blinding us. Having so many points afflicting us all at the same time and not taking the time to put them in order will eventually cause us to become extinct, just like the dinosaurs.

What would it take to make humanity understand that time is short? Do we have the time to spend just thinking about it or talking about it? On the other hand, is it time to start doing something about it… In fact, humans are always procrastinating about everything. However, this problem requires action, not procrastination, because it means the survival of our species as we know it.

Planet Earth has been around for four point five billion (4.5) years. During that time, it has been able to recycle itself many times, preserving life on it as we know it. It has a life of its Own. In addition, those that have the intelligence to keep it clean and ensure the continuation of its cycle lack the foresight to prevent it from happening.

# ONE MAN'S OPINION

What is it going to take before we face the fact that we will not have a position in space that we can call home? Certainly, it is a simple matter; we begin to do something about it now or wait until it is too late. Deciding on the latter will bring us to extinction. Everyone likes to sit around their kitchen table and propose all the possible answers and solutions they may predict. However, until this happens, there will be no progress. Some of the brightest minds in the World are now beginning to realize that we have a significant problem facing us. Talking about it is not going to produce results. We need action, and we need it now… For the average person on the streets, his primary concern is his daily survival. How am I going to make it until tomorrow? That is what is in his and her mind. While others just do not care, only because it should be managed by those that have the resources. United in Surviving should be the general goal for humanity.

Ethnic groups have their own agenda concerned with and can care less about what happens to the other groups.

People no longer care about their brothers or neighbors. As a result, we live in everlasting fear of what our future holds for us. As I see it, it is not too promising because no one is paying any attention to the signs given every day by our planet. Take a good look and see what is happening; the Planet is getting warmer and warmer, the Sea level is rising, and the weather patterns are getting more unstable. Causing unpredictable storms all over the World:

My theory is as follows; the deserts that are now on our planet are eating away at our fertile land increases as time moves on. At the rate of ten (10) feet every ten years at this rate, it will not be too long before we have any fertile land on this planet.

Rising oceans will erode most of the coastal lines of all the continents and countries. Making some of them disappear underwater. For example, the coast of the United States, both east and west, will see the ocean come in a few miles inland. Any major city within those boundaries will surely disappear underwater. New York City, and other cities along the eastern coastline down to the state of Florida, as well as the west coast, will disappear under fifty to one hundred feet of seawater. Florida as we know it will no longer exist. It will disappear. With the entire coastline along the Gulf of Mexico, with the Gulf of Mexico pushing inward towards the upper middle parts of the United States by New Orleans and the Mississippi River cutting the US in half:

The Islands in the Caribbean Ocean are becoming smaller, if not disappearing: The Island of Cuba will become much smaller. Only its highest peaks will show above the waters. Haiti and Santo Domingo, as well as Puerto Rico, will no longer exist; they will be gone. Just the tip of some of their tallest peak may stick out from the ocean, becoming uninhabitable and void of life.

A grim picture of the global map, yet, the only concern

people have today is how much money they are going to have in their bank account. How much they may owe the IRS, or whether they are going to hold on to their small fortune. That is happening today in countries like Africa and other parts of the World, where food shortages and the food they receive from other countries are not finely divided, creating vast numbers of people to continue to go hungry. In addition, causing humans, in the thousands, to starve to death.

These countries have exhausted the fertile land where they planted their crops, which can no longer bear fruits. They get little, if any, rain, which is also a contributing cause adding to their problem. Having all this all at once can be devastating to any country.

The energy crisis is another problem afflicting humanity. In addition, it will be around until another crisis pops up, and another, and another. Something we should be paying attention to now.

The most significant problem, which concerns me, is the lack of pure drinking water ($H_2O$). How long before we run out of it? Regardless of how much of the Arctic or Antarctic ice melts, it will not solve the water shortage; this is another problem we are facing today. There will be a time when man will give up his entire fortune just for a glass of pure, clear, clean water. Nations will go to war to control the rights to it. Conservation of our most valuable, water being one of the most significant, should be our immediate concern. The rate at which the human race is consuming our water today without any means to find a way to renew it will have disastrous results in our future.

Many countries are now feeling that their water supply is dwindling. Seeing this happening, humankind continues his search to self-destruct, knowing well that it will not be too long before there is no water to drink. When that happens, humankind will recognize the Earth is turning into a vast desert in space.

Global Warming is a fact, not a figment of someone's imagination. It's reality, and no one is paying attention. You hear about it every day, people talking on the radio, you see it on television, and even when people call each other on their phones, all you hear is the Earth is getting warmer. Soon there will not be any place to cool off.

I would think that some smart person would produce the idea of having cooling stations all over the country in our cities where people can pay a fee and have a way of cooling off. Used as public water fountains and public toilets found in many city parks. These stations must be under government control. The clock is ticking, and time is running out.

The United States, being the country it is, will likely inspire the private sector to introduce the concept.

# Analyzing Your Profession in Police Work as a Police Chief

Leadership is about control in developing a vision for the future; strategy achieves the vision. Thinking strategically about your company is a defining skill of top managers. Agency managers use critical thinking, which leads to strategic intent and will always project a vision of the future to improve where the company is heading. These reasons can ensure any company reaches the higher peak of incompetence and achieve its goals.

Drawing from my own life experiences has brought me to understand the business I worked for; being part of the group, which is law enforcement, is performing at peak strategic thinking, which is "Level three- (3)." The reason, it is a stable company with a minor change.

With a sound budget, good recourses and striving to be the best in the field, the company moves forward in meeting its new challenges in a positive way to erase resistance from competitors.

Police agencies strive to improve their situation concerning their rivals (competitors), and other Police Agencies, by using different tactics to secure a position in the community. The ability of an organization to prosper depends on how well it can deal with a number of causes at its disposal.

Agencies throughout the country, by introducing collective strategies, have been able to deal with rapid changes resulting in a more cheerful outlook on the part of their employees.

When discussing contemporary issues and a plan is in motion, these logical qualities come into play. "VISSION, MISSION, GOALS, STRATEGIES, TACTICS, and ACTION PLANS" By having top police administrators, being able to detect and distinguish between the "USE STRATEGY APPROACHES – vs. – USE OPPORTUNITY APPROACH" has made the Law Enforcement industry more stable and able to deal with the emerging trend. We must focus on central areas of responsibility that police administrators must deal with.

The duties of the Police Chief are as follows:

- Has the ability to supervise the Police Department by providing direction, guidance, and training to the Police Deputy Chief, Assistant Chief, Lieutenants, Sergeants, Officers, and support staff.
- Cooperate with other law enforcement agencies in all phases of police work.
- Remain current on court decisions and exciting law enforcement.

- Become knowledgeable on all Department and City policies and rules, Including State Statutes and local ordinances, and periodically update agency manuals.

- Prepare the annual department budget, ensuring the City Manager is aware of the needs of the agency.

- Recommend and take legal disciplinary action according to Civil Service Rules and administrative policies of the Department.

- Perform evaluations on Police Lieutenants, and review all other evaluations filed for employees in the Department.

- Assist in investigating crimes and other matters by conducting search and seizure and presenting evidence to ensure that employees have the necessary resources to succeed in the investigations.

- Provide information to the public about filing complaints.

- Take the correct action to ensure employees are following the Memorandum of Understanding as it the complaint and ensure both public and officer rights.

- Drive a Police car, either day or night, while communicating over police radio channels.

- Ensure Emergency Management readiness, as it applies to Law Enforcement work.

- Respond to issues raised by the City Manager and City Council on all police matters involving the City, as requested.
- Plan and supervise training programs for all Department employees.
- Take part in the multiagency training programs set up.
- Conduct or supervise Internal Affairs Investigations into any breach of duty or inefficiency by any Department personnel.
- Assist in selecting Patrol Officers and promotional positions in the Department, following all Civil Service rules and State law.
- Attend Civil Service Commission meetings as needed.
- Conduct or assigns staff to do tours of the Police station.
- Take part in interdepartmental planning, research, and training.
- Provide community education, crime prevention, and public relations programs for Law Enforcement to uphold a safe community.
- Work with all local news media and upholds a positive image in proving reasonable rules for news releases.
- Serve as Acting City Manager if requested.
- Research, draft, and manage grant applications.
- Perform other related duties as assigned.
- Knowledge, Skills, and Abilities.

- Ability to plan, layout, and supervise the work of several subordinates performing various police roles.
- Ability to set up and preserve working with other City officials, County, State and Federal authorities, and the public.
- Ability to react calmly in emergency cases.
- Ability to keep records and prepare reports.
- Ability to communicate effectively both verbally and in writing.
- Ability to teach an understanding of sound fiscal management practice in handling a departmental budget.
- Knowledge of the types and uses of firearms, communications, and automotive equipment used in modern police work.
- Administrators with these people skills can manage a police agency successfully.

# In Search of Sam

"Officer, I am not going to give you a tough time if you arrest me. It will do me good. Besides, I haven't had anything to eat for a few days, and in jail, I'll eat, get a few days' rest and a shower."

As I remember, in 1990, these were the first words Sam said to me. He had just gotten out of prison for allegedly committing burglary. I could not help feeling bad because I was the Officer who had put him there in the first place.

When I last spoke to him, he looked unhappy. It was before Christmas when everyone was running around buying Christmas gifts for their love-ones and friends. He told me that he had been in prison, where they had mistreated him.

He told me he had been thinking about me because he had been without food several times and, by going to prison, he was able to eat, get some long-needed sleep and shower. When he said that, I became speechless. I could not respond to what I had just heard.

I just stood there looking at him quietly for a few moments. I remained this way for a while. He then asked me what the problem was; I said to him, "Sam, there is no problem. I just wish I could be more helpful" His response was, "Silver Fox, you have done for me more in such a brief time than anybody has ever done before. Especially at the stage I find myself in. Causing everyone to look the other way and not to feel guilty for the condition I am in. People have this idea that by giving charity to the homeless, they can remove their consciousness and be able to sleep at night. How wrong they are."

Despite the fact I had been the Officer, who had put him in prison, he still had no resentment or held any grudge against me. Instead, he said I was doing my job while being sensitive to his needs. He felt that a representative of the establishment was not treating him as a bum; instead, looked at him as a human being. In fact, Sam was a good person with a good honest heart, and he had sincere feelings for others. However, being homeless was coincidental.

Being a police officer, working with, and assisting a good portion of the population, I learned meeting homeless people was teaching me a lot. There are all kinds of people from all lifestyles who are homeless. A solution with more creativity is essential for preventing these crises from becoming the norm. Unless you have just hit the lottery or you are a member of a wealthy family, you are but a paycheck away from being homeless.

People today do not understand that they spend fortunes yearly buying toilet paper or unnecessary items rather than spending some of that fortune feeding the misfortunate such as the homeless. I would like to see the phrase misfortunate-ones replace the phrase homeless from the dictionary.

In a wealthy society like ours, with good medicine and more than enough to care for everyone's needs, it is a disgrace to have people with nowhere to live or nothing to eat. Forcing them to go searching through garbage cans, recovering anything they can find just to survive.

As I got into deeper conversations with Sam, I found out just how intelligent and educated he was. Every word that came out of his mouth was full of logic. What impressed me the most about him was that he was always polite and chose his words carefully.

In moments of solitude, I often find myself reminiscing about my exploits when I was a police officer. Many times, thought enters my mind about Sam if he's still alive or if he has been a victim of a crime against the homeless, from people that just dislike the homeless because they are homeless. Whenever I see the news on TV or read articles about what is happening to the homeless right away, I think of Sam. My regret is that I did not take the time, as I should have learned more about this man.

Sam and I would engage in deep conversations about men's overall philosophy about the future of humankind. In addition, he would tell me and give me his views on how he felt the world was heading. In being a former attorney, he was familiar with the abuse of man against man.

As a result, I took a liking to him, and I offered to help him if he ever got into serious trouble. However, he never asks for my advice. In fact, he had so much pride that I could do nothing to help him even if I tried.

I realized then the reason everyone knew him was that he was homeless and living out on the street, naturally blamed for crimes occurring in the neighborhood.

The people were always accusing him of crimes committed in the area without being the ones responsible. Whenever I responded to a burglary in that city section, his name would always come up. I always looked forward to talking to him to figure out what caused him to be in that condition.

Sam was a private and sensitive person. He kept himself isolated from others, and there was an aura of secrecy about him, which I found interesting.

During the years I worked in the North District of the City of Miami, while on my way to work; I would always see him at the intersection corner of Northwest 6 Avenue and 79 Street. It was like clockwork. I could almost set my watch on his schedule. He was always there, rain or shine. It did not make any difference; he would always be there trying to make a dollar in helping clean motorist windshields so he could eat.

I cannot help thinking about him because as I continued to

know him, he revealed more of himself. He began to let out more of his true feelings and about his experiences; I then realized being homeless is no shame. As I recall, he was a good decent human being; he was an African American short in stature. One day he asked me if I had time to listen to a story. I replied, "Is it going to take all day?" He answered, "No," So I began to listen.

He began by telling me his name. His true name was Samuel Jones's Constantine; he was born in a small town in Southern Mississippi from a small family and was the youngest of two brothers and a sister. He continued by telling me how he had lost both of his siblings months apart during the Vietnam War.

This tragic event of losing two loving family members in such a brief time brought great stress and suffering on his parents, so much so that they also died the same year.

Sam said he was 16 years old at the time. He was young, full of dreams and hopes, and fond of his two brothers. He loved them dearly. He never thought for once that his best two friends, which he looked up to with great admiration and respect, would be gone from his life in such a brief time. Leaving him an empty hollow shell.

For Sam, his biggest ambition was to finish his education, go on to college, and become a productive citizen in his community. That is what his parents would have wanted.

His sister went off, married her High School boyfriend, and raised a family. They moved out west somewhere in California. At times, he would write to her just to see how she was doing. However, she never wrote back. After a while, he just stopped writing.

Sam's dream was to become an Attorney. He got himself a job, worked hard at night, and with little sleep, went to school during the day. This went on for five years. He finally graduated from Law School, passed the Mississippi Bar examination, and became a successful, prominent Attorney in the state of Mississippi.

He went on to marry a college sweetheart and had two children, a boy and a girl. Both kids took after their father's footsteps and went on to Law School. They also became successful and found their rightful place in society. Sam was living the American dream a fine house, a beautiful wife and two well-adjusted kids.

He told me that, during those years, he felt he was entitled to the finest things life had to offer, and he was going to try to get them. However, like everything in life, all that is good eventually ends.

He told me that whenever he got lovable and tried to caress his wife, she would push him away. She began staying out late at night with her girlfriends. This was causing friction on both. His marriage between him and his wife was falling apart. He did not know what to make of it. This went on for many years until he became dissolution with her.

He tried every way that he could make their situation better, but it was not working. When he was about to walk out on her, he began thinking what a good husband he had been. He felt if he would just hold on a little while longer, maybe things would get better between them, and things could go back to the way they used to be, but it did not happen. He began to blame himself for the failure of his marriage and for not being there for his wife's needs. However, after several tries, it did not turn out the way he wanted.

One day, Sam came home. Walked into his house, straight into his bedroom and lay down. He felt that he needed some sleep after a stressful day in court. After a few hours had passed, he said that his wife had walked into the bedroom while he was sleeping. He suddenly woke up by the sound of her footsteps, startled as if he had just woken up from a bad dream.

He became upset; he told me he had asked her why she was standing by the side of the bed, and she had replied, "I don't know, Sam." when she walked away, he asked her again, and she answered she wanted a divorce. He said he became upset, asking her again why she wanted a divorce, and she replied she did not love him anymore and there was no reason for them to continue living together. All she wanted was out of the marriage.

Sam felt devastated and betrayed by her actions and behavior. Never did he ever dream that this could happen to him.

During those minutes, which Sam said, seemed like an eternity, his whole life fell apart, collapsing in front of him. It was as if someone had just pulled the rug from underneath his feet. He could not find words to express his sorrow. He just kept quiet, walked out of the bedroom, and kept on walking out of the house until he found himself in the street.

Weeks passed, finding himself with nothing to eat, to live out of garbage cans just to survive. Even his kids forgot about him.

They made no effort to find him to see if he were all right. Sam felt abandoned. This caused a momentous change in Sam's attitude and his perspective on life.

The first time I met Sam, he had been standing underneath a broken-down wooden shed with the roof partially gone from storms that ravaged the city days before. He looked bruised and as if in pain. He told me men had beaten him days before without any reason, and they just walked away laughing at him.

Earlier that day, it had been raining hard, like buckets falling from the sky. It had rained a lot. Most of the areas were still flooded from rain days before. It was in the early part of winter in December. It was a cold and rainy night. He was shivering out of control from the cold, of being wet, and out all night with nothing to eat. It is not pleasant to find yourself in that situation. I could not imagine ever finding myself in that same situation. It was heart-wrenching for me to see this creature of a human being standing there. Sick, cold, beaten, and hungry, I had to do something.

As I drove up and approached him in my squad car, I could see him in the distance shivering from the cold and looking pitiful. I stopped my police car, got out, walked to the rear, and opened the trunk. I pulled out an old but still-good heavy jacket I had in the trunk of my car and gave it to him. It was all I could do besides giving him a few dollars to get him by for a few days.

As I started walking away, I noticed in his eyes that he was full of gratitude and grateful for what I had just done for him. As he thanked me, he began to cry. I told him not to cry, and he stopped. He looked at me as if surprised at what I was doing.

He could not believe someone was taking the time to care for a needy person in distress. Months passed, and during that time, I must have arrested him almost ten times. All for the same reason, Suspicion of burglary and other misdemeanors.

The day he saw me, he said to me, "It just goes to show you, Silver Fox, life is full of surprises. Here you are. One day you are helping me, and the next, you are putting me in jail. Life is funny, isn't it?" I replied, "That's what life is all about, Sam; don't try to make any sense out of it because if you do, it will drive you crazy." He laughed, shook his head in disbelief and walked away.

I knew he was grateful for what I had done for him. He told

me that he had been up there with the rich and famous and, in becoming overwhelmed with such success, had fallen into homelessness. Nevertheless, never forgot his pride and integrity. He was able to manage to hold on to his sanity because of his love for life. He was able to accept his new reality in life in which he found himself.

Sam was a realist, practical person. He never complained, even after I had arrested him so many times for being singled out as the offender of several burglaries in the area. Incidents he claimed he had never done. However, because of the laws in our society, I needed to comply with the wishes of the community in arresting him.

One reason for which I was proud, I took a reasonable amount of time to get to know Sam and his beliefs. He was a product of our times. A part of an overlooked segment of society that no one wants to deal with and just ignore. The homeless problem is a significant one, a taboo subject that no one wants to touch because it is too sensitive in nature. Since no one has a solution, no one wants to get involved.

Now everyone is too busy focusing on unimportant issues that no one pays attention to the homeless problem. We as humans should never allow ourselves to forget to take the time to get to know our siblings who might be in need. Whether we like it or not, we, as part of humanity, have inherited the grave responsibility of being our brother's keeper.

We have an investment in a commitment to help those who are in need. After all, our duty as professional police officers is to be objectively fair, treat everyone equally and respect them regardless of their status. We should all practice what we preach. By taking a moment to help our friends, brothers, and sisters by guiding them in the right direction, we will inspire more love in this world. When helping anyone, it should be unconditional without any regard to race, color, or creed, expecting nothing in return.

Today, we have the expertise and the means to erase the homeless problem. However, we lack the willpower to commit ourselves. We should all put our pride in the trashcan and go with what is important in life, which is to help our fellow man.

It has been sixteen years since I last saw Sam, and during that time, I have wondered how he must be doing. If he is sick or suffered an accident, I am hoping he is all right. I am sure wherever he is, he is just as caring now as he was then, only a great deal older.

Sam, wherever you are, I hope that these few lines get to you so you will understand and realize the positive impact you had on my life. This I will cherish for the rest of my life. Remember, Sam, what happened to you can happen to anyone regardless of their financial success in life.

Sam, since I last saw you, I have been searching for you with limited success. I will continue to search for you with the hope of finding you someday. To be able to look straight into your eyes, my friend, and say to you, "Welcome home, my brother, it's good to see you again."

Again, I say to you, Sam, that falling from grace and being homeless is no shame. Please try not to hold any grudges against police officers that you may encounter because they are just doing their job.

I retired from the Police force Sam, and I am enjoying my free time with my grandchildren. I am also in a better position to help you if you ever need my help.

I wish your health, my friend, with the hope of meeting you again so we can talk about the old days again… I would like to take the time to buy you a cup of coffee for old-time's sake, friend!

# The Steam Kettle Rocket

Paying attention to simple techniques in physics in using simple ideas, such as the steam engine, we could venture further into the outer regions of our Universe without difficulties. Water tanks made of thick, heavy-duty titanium steel that would withstand enormous pressure, attach nozzles, fill them with seawater, and freeze it. Attach a control valve at the end of each nozzle controlling the release of the heated pressure.

Consider these tanks, attach them to rockets sent into space and store them at the International Space Station for future use. Keeping them in orbit around the Earth, you could use them as the propellant fuel for travel to Mars.

These tanks attached to the spacecraft would propel them on a journey to any destination in space. Releasing the steam pressure satisfactorily will control the speed of the spacecraft while in flight. Once the spacecraft is in motion out in space, it will continue its journey until stopped. On a trip to Mars, the tanks could be refilled with, preferably seawater or salty water found on the planet, by freezing it to use on the return trip to Earth.

In theory, a cluster of these tanks filled with frozen seawater could remain in orbit and attach to the space station for future strips to the outer regions in space. The use of these tanks could be an inexpensive method of propellant fuel for future space travel. The next step would be a simple matter of getting the Astronauts and a spacecraft like our space shuttle out in orbit. Attaching these tanks as a means of the propellant to the space shuttle and, in theory, could propel the space shuttle on a journey to any near region in space. This method of propellant could replace the dangerous and expensive ones used today.

During my research, while conducting my experiments, I made several small workable samples of a steam engine. The first one was a small steam kettle, to which I attached a small gauge to it to give me readings of the pressure inside the kettle. I then attached a small variable control valve at the end of the nozzle. I filled the kettle with water and placed it in the freezer overnight.

The following day I connected the kettle with the frozen water to a roller skate with four little wheels. I then began applying heat to it with a burning torch. Watching the gauge for the proper reading, I saw the kettle starting to shake and inflate like a balloon. Afraid that it was going to blow up, I stopped applying heat. I then carefully started opening the valve. As I did, the kettle began to move in the opposite direction from where the steam was escaping. The more I opened the valve, the faster the kettle moved forward. Showed me the same principle would work out in space if applied to the spacecraft.

The second experiment was the same thing; it was done with

one exception I made the kettle much stronger and able to withstand more stress. In doing so, I got the same results as the first one but much more potent in pressure. The gauge read a greater pressure, double the pressure from the first one. Converting frozen water into steam, the first kettle almost began to break apart, while the second held tight with no signs of stress because it was stronger and thicker.

Further experiments showed using water with a higher concentration of salt caused the water to boil hotter with more pressure making it a better source of fuel. Using Seawater would be more practical because of its abundance throughout the World. More likely also in other planets as well.

This experiment showed space travel to be less expensive and reliable, reducing the time of getting the spacecraft's further regions in space.

# The Age of Innocence

The sixties were an era of high distress and confusion. Yet, despite the horrific events taking place during that time, it was the age of innocence. There was an unpopular War waging across a large ocean in a Country that few people knew little about. The country, which had been at war with France and had known war for generations, a country in which the United States, in trying to help bring democracy, became entangled with its internal affairs, having unpleasant outcomes.

It was a time when there were demonstrations across our Nation, dividing the country. Still, it was an era rich with charm and grace, a time of innocence when hippies and flower people held hands while protesting the war. It was a period for giving, an era of caring, an era for forgiving. The hippie's philosophy was to love your next-door neighbor, not meddle in other countries' affairs, and smoke grass.

A time when there was a War, which caused the US thousands of lives with nothing to show for it but a black marble wall in Washington DC with over fifty-eight thousand names on it. A time when family members would gather on weekend BBQs to discuss the War that was unpopular and gather their thoughts about the future that lay ahead.

We had the youngest president ever elected, John Fitzgerald

Kennedy. A man with dreams cut short by lunatics' bullet whose ideology and twisted agenda we will never know. It was supposed to have been the era of "Camelot" for this country. It was a time in our nation's history when it was going through a transition period, and everyone was full of doubts while at the same time filled with hopes. A time when democracy was at its highest and people's rights were evaluated. The war had a gravely negative impact on the economy, creating high disparity among our younger generation. It was the age of the Supremes, Otis Redding's, the Impressions, Mamas and the Papas, and many other fine groups, which kept our young people and our nation, regardless of the war, dancing and happy. It was an era of warm love when everyone cared for one another; it was an age of innocence.

During the war, I was still in High School. I was working part-time as a stockroom clerk boy in a Mama and Papa Pharmacy earning ten dollars a week. Out of my salary, I was able to pay two dollars a week for my mother's washing machine she had bought, and I still had enough to take my girlfriend to the movies on the weekends.

However, when I saw my best friends come home in body bags, I decided it was time for me to do my part in sharing the responsibility for going to Vietnam. I attended several funerals of a friend with whom I had gone to school and gone many parties. I realized then I would not sit idle while my friends were killed in a foreign land.

I pulled my father and Mother; aside, and I told them I needed to make a difference and that I was not going to stand by while watching my friends die. Both my parents did not like the idea; however, after explaining to them the importance of helping my country, they understood.

It was a hot period during that summer school vacation in July 1962. Most fire hydrants throughout the city were opened by young kids trying to keep cool. I was one of them. I was desperate; it was hot, and nothing to do. Most of my friends had already left and joined the army. Most had already left for Vietnam. On July 11, 1962, I decided to go downtown to the Army recruiting station in lower Manhattan, Whitehall Street and signed up.

After a series of academic tests and psychological evaluations, I took my oath. I was proud on that day because I knew in a few days, I was on my way to the Army training base at Fort Dix, New Jersey. When the day finally arrived, I was full of gratitude, knowing I was going to contribute my share in the fight alongside my body.

I spent sixteen weeks in training. The first eight weeks were basic Infantry the second eight weeks were in Advance Infantry training. I graduated as a heavy weapons specialist and went to Fort Benning, Georgia, where I received my training as an elite

# REINALDO IRIZARRY

Paratrooper.

After graduating from paratrooper school, I went to the elite 101st. Airborne Division, "C" Company, 327 Infantry First Battalion First Brigade, the "Screaming Eagles" at Fort Campbell, Kentucky.

# How do we identify the Enemy?

In today's World, in which we live, who is the enemy? What does he look like? How do we recognize him? What do we look for to identify him? Once we identify him, how do we stop him? These are fundamental questions that our government should be asking, are we going to be successful in managing the coming anarchies that lie ahead for us? Our next-door neighbor could be checking us out, just waiting for the moment to kill us.

It is a fact; humans have been waging war against one another since the beginning of time. They have not developed a harmonious way of living and sharing this planet, which is the only planet we have. As a result, they have fought each other for ages with little regard for the value of life.

Since the beginning days of the Bible, Brother has attacked Brother with the intent of killing him. If Families kill each other, what makes you think that neighbors would be any different?

Family members should support and love one another because they come from the same family inner circle, such as a mother and father. However, that is not always the case. At times, during periods of hostilities, our neighbors can be more dependable than our own families. However, this is a problem because of the way the world is today, so whom can you trust?

In early warfare, the enemy would face each other in battle. One will try to be victorious over the other. Countries would wage war where there were boundaries. You knew where the enemy was, and you could destroy him; that is no longer the case in today's battles; our soldiers do not know who the enemy is. They come disguised with a smile on their faces. They are of assorted colors, ages, gender, and religion and look much like us. They dress like us; they believe in family values like us; they practice their religion like us. Yet because of differences in religious beliefs in not understating their differences, we participate in a conflict which will last for a long time in the Middle East and have been fighting one another for ages. Not because of economic reasons but because of religious beliefs.

Their religious ideology is what governs their lives and form of government. They have not thought about the word freedom. Ruled by forms of government comprised of Monarchies, Kings and Queens, Warlords, and Tyrants who had the power and money to pay armies so they could hold onto power. They would pass it down to their heirs and children at the time of their deaths.

Having engaged in many wars, the U.S., with good intelligence in identifying its enemy and quickly adapting to its strategy, has been successful in its victories. That has been the case with most wars the U.S. has fought. In allowing our Generals and high military ranking personnel with experience in the art of

Warfare to do the planning and setting War plans in motion, not the politicians who are sitting behind a desk in Washington with no military experience.

There have been instances where we have made a mistake in having our Politicians dictate the tactics used in battles, having to pull out to save face. The Vietnam War was a perfect example. I know I was there, and now we participate in another war that will take at least ten (10) years or more before we can have an idea of its outcome.

Because of the War in Iraq and the way the War is being managed, the rule of engagement has drastically changed, giving the enemy an edge over us. The enemy has his own set of rules of engagement during his battle against us, and that is to destroy us all. White, Black, Asians, Europeans, and not to forget the Jewish people, which the Muslim community would like to see disappear from the face of the Earth. It is either the Muslin way or the Highway.

During the Civil War, we knew who the enemy was. He was our friend and our own family in arms. There was a frontline, which changed back and forth during battles. Forcing both sides to set up strategic battle plans to find ways to defeat each other.

In future wars, there is not going to be a frontline. We are going to be fighting the enemy on our own front lawn. That is going to be after the radiation clouds scatter, and it is safe to go outside to fight. We are going to be in a fight that will last for years. There is not going to be any law and order on earth. Families will fight each other for food and water and whatever they can get from them. Total Anarchic, fighting and struggling just for the little piece of land they may have in front of them, which will be a safe space. This is what our future holds for us. That is what our human intelligence has brought us.

I believe that we, as Humans, are the inheritors of the Universe. In addition, we could spread our species across vast distances from one end of the universe to the other for all to enjoy... This is a gift from God, which he has given us, and we have failed to realize it. In addition, we continue to walk blinded by hatred with no love for one another. Instead, striving to get what others may have by force or intimidation.

# The Devil finally emerges

Allowing Pakistan to fall, it will be but a brief time before Nuclear Bombs rain down on the entire Middle East. The first country to disappear will be Israel, next Egypt; from that point, the whole region will go up in smoke. Once this happens, it will spread across the globe, influencing all humankind.

In moments of turmoil when countries are at the edge because of rumors of World War III, there is an overwhelming sense among inhabitants on this planet the Devil is finally emerging. What is happening in Pakistan, a country, which has experienced Democracy for some time, is a good example? At this point in history, it is taking a step backward in returning to totalitarian rule. The country, which has Nuclear Bombs and the resources to use them, finds it self-in readiness because of its internal confusion.

Complex inner Muslim organizations with the hope of turning the country upside down and taking over are influencing the turmoil which is taking place. Placing an arsenal of weapons at their disposal will complete their lifelong dream of creating havoc on Earth by destroying it.

Countries such as Russia, China, and Iran are just watching and waiting on what is happening in Pakistan. They all welcome these events because they selves in their best interest.

They are willing to sit around and do nothing while the region goes up in smoke. It is advantageous to them because they think they can walk in after the destruction, lend a helping hand in cleaning up the mess and get the credit. They are willing to do anything to keep the United States from receiving any world recognition for its involvement in bringing democracy and stability to the region.

Pakistan is a country that has been helping the United States in the struggle in fighting radical's Muslims, which is spreading across the world. In its internal struggle, it is obvious that various religious groups are waging war on one another to control the country.

These radical religious groups disguise themselves as political organizations to give a different face to their intents.

We are witnessing the end. In addition, the possibility for radicals like Bin Laden to use this as an excuse to take over the country. If he succeeds, we are in serious trouble. India, having the opportunity now to show Pakistan that it is concerned about its internal struggle instead of offering some support in preventing the government from falling, is not helping. It is taking a stance of doing nothing because it benefits its own political agendas. Giving them a reason to put their forces on high alert along its borders in case the turmoil spreads inland.

# ONE MAN'S OPINION

If Pakistan was allowed to fall, there would be a ripple domino effect across the entire Middle East region. Eventually will in golf the whole World-changing it, as we now know it. The World will have a different face, and it will not be a pleasant one.

# The Captains in Charge

It was a cool and bright Friday Morning on January 5, 2007. At 6:00 AM, my wife drove me to the Fort Lauderdale Airport to catch a flight scheduled to leave for Los Angeles, California, at 7:30 AM. We arrived at the Airport at 7:00 AM; I went through security lines boarding at 7:15. The plane left the grounds exactly at 7:30 AM. It arrived in Los Angeles at 1:00 PM. The flight lasted six long bumpy hours. When I arrived, I was hungry and tired. I did not eat because what they gave me on the plane was not worth eating.

While at the Airport, I was expecting the Chief to pick me up as he was supposed to. Instead, he sent his secretary; she was waiting to pick me up to take me to my hotel. She told me that he was not feeling well and was not able to make it, so he asked her to do him a favor and pick me up. She drove me to the Days Inn Hotel in Santa Monica, California. That was the closest Hotel to the VA Police Headquarters on Wilshire Boulevard, Los Angeles.

When I got to the Hotel, I rented a room for two weeks until I could find a suitable permanent place to live. The hotel room was small; what can you expect of the Hotel? However, the room they gave me the Air-condition was not working, and it smelled like dirty socks or like someone had died in the room. After complaining to the Manager, they changed my room to a much nicer one, with a better view across the street.

That Friday night was cold and windy, and I was not scheduled to report for work until Monday Morning. Therefore, for the next two days, I used my time to walk around and familiarize myself with the neighborhood. I also spent time looking for an inexpensive place to rent. The neighborhood was expensive and high-class. In those two days, I must have walked half of Los Angeles while working out a sweat. I finally found an apartment at Wilshire Boulevard in Brentwood, a small section of LA., near where O'Jay once lived.

The building was close to the police Headquarters where I was going to be working. I talked to the rental agent to see if I could rent a one-bedroom apartment. The agent told me there was one apartment scheduled to empty in two days if I needed it. I said yes. The rent was two thousand dollars a month with a three thousand dollar deposit. I had no other choice but to take it. I gave the agent the money, and I was scheduled to move in a week later.

I went back to the Hotel to sleep because I had been walking all day looking for a place, and I was tired of walking so much. During that week, while walking, I spent as little money as I could because I did not have that much money with me. The money I did have had to last me until my first paycheck. I got exercise by walking all over the neighborhood and sweating so much that it would last me a lifetime.

When Monday morning came, January 8, 2007, I was up early and ready to start my new career in Law Enforcement again. On that day, I walked to the Police Headquarters. When I arrived, the Chiefs Administrative Officer and members of his staff met me. They were polite in welcoming me into the Police family and making me feel comfortable.

They offered me coffee, which I accepted, and I sat down to relax and wait for the Chief to arrive. As I was waiting, I looked around at my surroundings to see the design of the room. I saw photos of the Chief and the men in a platoon formation. They looked sharp and neat.

There were other photos showing the landscape of the city and the significant buildings to keep an eye on because of sensitive items inside.

The place had the flavor of the old Police Station that you would usually find in a small town out West. The officers all looked sharp and well-dressed in all their equipment needed for the job. The Black and White Police cars parked outside in front of the police station. Clean and lined up as if they were ready for me to conduct an inspection.

They looked neat and professional. It showed the public the degree of professionalism the agency had. It was an impressive sight to look at. Even before the Chief hired me, I had spoken with him and explained to him that my plan was to give myself a ninety-day trial period to watch, listen, speak, and meet people for which I was responsible. I told him I needed the opportunity to evaluate the philosophy of the employees in the department for all of us to be on the same page. In addition, look at the existing problems in the department and determined if I were going to help him in removing them. I would then decide if I was going to stay or leave.

He was not happy with my plans. He wanted me for at least five years before I would choose if I would leave or stay. I said ninety days were plenty of time for any good manager to decide on staying or leaving.

The Administrative Officer was knowledgeable and gave me the rundown on the workings of the station. I walked around and looked at the layout of the building and the surroundings to learn my way around. They introduced me to the Lieutenant, who was going to be responsible for my first two weeks of in-house training.

He gave me instruction manuals, which I would need to familiarize myself with during the two weeks, eighty-hour training phase. After which, I would attend a six-week familiarization course at the Veterans Affairs Police Academy in Little Rock, Arkansas. He pulled me aside when the chief was not looking and would tell me how silly he felt giving instruction to a Captain who was going to be his supervisor. I told him that it was not a significant issue and not to think about it. He would laugh and walk away, showing a sense of relief. We became good friends and went out for lunch several times while I was with the agency.

For the next few weeks, during my training, I would watch, listen, and talk to the police employees to get to know them and the problems in the agency. The Police staff that was going to be under my supervision displayed a positive, receptive manner to my views and ideas for the agency. They expressed genuine concern about my interest, and they welcomed me warmly. They were helpful in letting me know what was troubling them. They welcomed the idea of having someone bring to the agency a cheerful outlook and share that attitude with them.

From the first day on the job, all I saw and heard were complaints about the Chief. They showed me how unhappy, discontent, and distrustful they felt. They did not approve of his methods of talking to people, and they rejected his methods of intimidation.

They said that he lacked people skills, which is an essential quality that a Police chief must have. They complained that he was not a fair Chief and that he would show favoritism to the people he liked. To my surprise, in the brief time, I was there, I did witness those qualities.

However, not to make a big issue out of it, I made it clear that I would do everything within my power to correct the inconsistencies taking place in the agency. In addition, to be patient with the Chief because eventually, it would get better, I further made it clear to them that my purpose in coming to the agency was to assist the Chief and help him manage the agency.

To encourage the workings of the unit and relieve him from the stress caused by the responsibilities of the job and help him supervise the police employees to increase the efficiency of the agency.

I met with the watch commanders and spoke with them. We discussed all kinds of possibilities at our disposal, which we could use to help us fix the problems causing the officers to feel left out of the choices made within the agency.

The distance from the Hotel and the Police Headquarters was five miles each way, ten miles total. That is how many miles I would walk every day, rain or shine, because I did not have a car. The Transit Authority was slow, and the waiting time at the bus stop was long. When they did come, they looked like sardine cans filled with people with no place to sit or stand.

Meanwhile, when the Chief found out I was walking to and from work every morning, he offered to help me by picking me up and taking me to work. Saving me from getting to the job late, hot, and full of sweat, which was an everyday affair; believe me, I was grateful for the gesture, but after a while, it became bothersome, and I rented a car. During the times he was driving me to work, he would tell me God had sent me to help him run the agency. That would always stick in my mind, and I became concerned about his mental faculties. However, he was a religious man, always mentioning God and bringing up religious topics, so I did not pay attention.

The men would complain to me about how he would walk into the front Police reception area, especially when it was full of people talking about Jesus Christ and how everyone should follow his teachings. They asked me to put a stop to it, a responsibility that I found almost impossible.

January 8, 2007, I assumed command of the Veterans Affairs Police Services patrol in Los Angeles, California. I was responsible for Sixty-five Officers, Six lieutenants, and Sixteen Sergeants. I commanded two Divisions, the North Division in the City of Sepulveda and the Downtown LA Division.

There was a forty-minute drive from Headquarters to my North Division. In addition, an hour's drive between the North Division and my Downtown LA Division. I would supervise the North Command in the morning and the Downtown Command in the afternoon. It kept me busy and on the road a lot. I found the police employees all knowledgeable officers with high education, and the majority were ex-military men. The workload, which was, spread evenly in the department, was the same as in any small Police Department in the city, and the crime rate was low.

The job gave me satisfaction and the opportunity to meet many interesting and relevant people involved in Law Enforcement. Such as Agents from Homeland Security, Federal Protective Service, DEA, Los Angeles Police Department, Loss Angeles County Sheriff's Department, People from the Loss Angeles state's Attorney's Office and Agents from the Office of the inspecting General in Washington DC.

I spent my time in meetings representing the Chief. This kept me away from my other duties, such as supervising my staff employees and police officers.

# Basic Creole for Police Officers

Communities throughout the United States and other countries are now realizing that Police agencies are closing the linguistic gap, which creates difficulties in communication between Police Departments and citizens. Through motivation and the creation of incentives, agencies are now producing a substantial number of Police officers seeking linguistic courses to be more efficient when responding to calls involving speaking groups.

It is a challenging task for Police Officers who work and patrol areas of Cities populated by different ethnic groups that speak different languages. If the officers do not know how to communicate with the citizens, it makes their job impossible.

It is desirable for Supervisors to assign officers who can understand and speak the language which is common in the area they work. For them to serve the community as needed, they must have a working knowledge of the language. Not understanding what people are saying when officers arrive at disturbances is frustrating. In most communities where there is a large part of the community, which holds on to their native ways by communicating in their own language, it can be a problem.

Most Police Agencies throughout the country have known for many years how important it is for officers to be bilingual. Not just in the United States, but other countries as well are now

74

realizing it and are setting linguistic sessions so their officers can experience it when dealing with different organizations.

Therefore, in using part of the people, for example, Creole-speaking citizens, it would be most proper to have Police Officers trained in basic terms in Creole to help them communicate with the citizens in the community. This will make Officers experienced, making them efficient in performing their job satisfactorily.

The following are some essential terms and phrases useful for Police officers who are working in Haitian communities.

## DAYS OF THE WEEK:

English:                                            Creole:

Sunday,                                            Dimanch

Monday,                                           Lendi

Tuesday,                                          Madi

Wednesday,                                    Mekredi

Thursday,                                        Jedi

Friday,                                            Vandredi

| Saturday, | Samdi |
|-----------|-------|

## MONTHS OF THE YEAR:

| English: | Creole: |
|----------|---------|
| January, | Janvye |
| February, | Fevriye |
| March, | Mas |
| April, | Avril |
| May, | Me |
| June, | Jen |
| July, | Jiye |
| August, | Out |
| September, | Septanm |
| October, | Oktob |
| November, | Novanm |
| December, | Desanm |

## **NUMBERS:**

| English: | Creole: |
|---|---|
| 0 – Zero | 0 – Zewo |
| 1 – One | 1 – En |
| 2 – Two | 2 – De |
| 3 – Three | 3 – Twa |
| 4 – Four | 4 – Kat |
| 5 – Five | 5 – Senk |
| 6 – Six | 6 – Sis |
| 7 – Seven | 7 – Set |
| 8 – Eight | 8 – Wit |
| 9 – Nine | 9 – Nef |
| 10 – Ten | 10 – Dis |
| 11 – Eleven | 11 – Onz |
| 12 – Twelve | 12 – Douz |
| 13 – Thirteen | 13 – Trez |

| | |
|---|---|
| 14 – Fourteen | 14 – Katoz |
| 15 – Fifteen | 15 – Kenz |
| 16 – Sixteen | 16 – Sez |
| 17 – Seventeen | 17 – Diset |
| 18 – Eighteen | 18 – Dizwit |
| 19 – Nineteen | 19 – Diznef |
| 20 – Twenty | 20 – Ven |
| 21 – Twenty-one | 21 – Venteyen |
| 22 – Twenty-two | 22 – Vennde |
| 23 – Twenty-three | 22 – Venndetwa |
| 24 – Twenty-four | 24 – Nenndekat |
| 25 – Twenty-five | 25 – Venndesenk |
| 26 – Twenty-six | 26 – Venndesis |
| 27 – Twenty-seven | 27 – Venndeset |
| 28 – Twenty-eight | 28 – Venndewit |
| 29 – Twenty-nine | 29 – Venndenef |
| 30 – Thirty | 30 – Trant |
| 40 – Forty | 40 – Karant |
| 50 – Fifty | 50 – Senkant |

| | |
|---|---|
| 60 – Sixty | 60 – Swasant |
| 70 – Seventy | 70 – Swasantdis |
| 80 – Eighty | 80 – Katreven |
| 90 – Ninety | 90 – Katrevendis |
| 100 – One-hundred | one hundred – San |
| 101 – One-hundred-one | 101 – San-en |
| 102 – One-hundred-two | 102 – Sande |
| 200 – Two-hundred | two hundred – Desan |
| 300 – Three-hundred | three hundred – Twasan |
| 400 – Four-hundred | four hundred – Katsan |
| 500 – Five-hundred | five hundred – Senksan |
| 600 – Six-hundred | six hundred – Sisan |
| 700 – Seven-hundred | seven hundred – Setsan |
| 800 – Eight-hundred | eight hundred – Wisan |
| 900 – Nine-hundred | nine hundred – Nefsan |
| 1000 – One-thousand | one thousand – Mil |

## COMMON EXPRESSIONS DURING THE DAY:

| English | Creole |
|---|---|
| Yesterday, | ye |
| This Morning, | maten – a |
| Now, | konnye – a |
| This Afternoon, | apre – midi - a |
| Today, | Jodi – a |
| Tonight, | Nan nwit – la |
| Tomorrow, | denmen |
| This Evening, | a – swe - a |
| Last Night, | ye swa |
| Last week, | semen pase |
| Last Month, | mwa pase |
| In the Morning, | Nan maten |
| In the Afternoon, | nana premidi |
| In the Evening, | a swa |

## FAMILY MEMBERS.

| English: | Creole: |
|---|---|
| Grandfather, | gran pe |
| Grandmother, | gran me |
| Father, | papa |
| Mother, | manman |
| Brother, | fre |
| Sister, | se |
| Grandson, | pitit |
| Granddaughter, | pitit |
| Fiancé, | fiyanse |
| Bride, | la marye |
| Bridegroom, | le marye |
| Husband, | Mari |
| Wife, | madanm |
| Children, | to mou yo |
| Son, | pitit gason |
| Daughter, | piti fi |

| Daughter–in–law, | bel fi |
|---|---|
| Brother–in–law, | bofre |
| Sister – in – law, | belse |
| Stepfather, | bofe |
| Stepmother, | belme |
| Relatives, | fanmi paran |
| Aunt, | tant |
| Uncle, | tonton |

## POSSESSIVES.

| English: | Creole. |
|---|---|
| My, | pa – m |
| Your, | pa – ou |
| His, | pa – 1 |
| Hers, | pa – 1 |
| Ours, | pa – nou |

# Nature of Police Work

In Police work, officers involve ninety percent of the time in managing small disturbances dealing with no criminal matters. Incidents that police officers do not enforce. The other ten percent deals with calls involving serious incidents.

Police work involves the protection of life, safeguarding property through vigorous patrol techniques, and enforcement of laws and ordinances in the Cities for which the Police Agency is responsible.

The job requires officers to posse's characteristics involving dedication to the profession. Not all people in Police work are there for the same purpose. There are several reasons given by officers why they seek this line of work.

Officers who are out in the street during their tour of duty are combat officers. They are the first's line of defense between the criminals and the citizens of the community. During their tour of duty, unexpectedly, they may well be in a crisis without any warning. These officers are who respond to calls for assistance and, during downtime, do police work while looking for reported trouble areas.

On a routine day, officers can go for hours without responding to any significant emergency incident, forcing officers to do aggressive patrols looking for criminals. During these times, is when unexpectedly, everything turns upside down. In most cases, officers are seriously injured; some die because of their injuries. One moment all is calm and peaceful; the next, it may have bullets flying in every direction.

Officers receive specialized training in various fields, such as Police Community Relations, School Officers, and Field Training Officers, through advanced education needed by their departments. Police officers receive special assignments in plainclothes involving investigations dealing with drugs or intelligence gathering for future missions.

Police officers are concerned with a call, which requires them to be skilled in their field of expertise, which is the way; they can achieve status within their peer's organization. Police work involves the responsibility of performing various routine police assignments.

They usually consist of a routine patrol in emergency police cars, Bicycles, Motorcycles, Horse Mounties, Marine boats, and on foot patrol. Some believe Police work is just like in the movies, where the Cops near the end of the movie always catch the bad guy. They think they can walk away with the catch prize, the leading woman in the movie, and even try to get rich by doing illegal acts.

This only happens in the movies. Bad guys usually escape

and are caught days later. In addition, the offices return the next day to their routine, mundane police work.

The job involves danger needing the officer to perform without direct supervision and exercise independent judgment in meeting emergencies.

Supervisors issue assignments and review work methods and results through reports. Conduct employee inspections and discussions with their officers.

Uniform Police Officers patrol appointed areas in Cities in an Emergency police cruiser to maintain law and order, prevent and discover the commission of crimes, and enforce traffic laws. Answer calls for service and complaints involving disturbances.

They perform the preliminary investigations in the zones assigned previously given to the Detective Bureau for follow-up and final resolution. They testify in court as a professional witness. At the crime scene, officers were required to perform first aid when there was an injured person. While waiting for rescue, conduct a preliminary investigation, gather evidence of the crime, safeguard the evidence, get witnesses, and make an arrest.

By using specialized investigative procedures, Field Combat Officers are the first responders to calls for service involving the following:

- Burglaries

- Domestic disturbances

- Grand Theft

- Homicide

- Missing People

- Robberies

- Sexual Battery (Rape)

- Traffic Accidents

Basic needs for Police Officers:

- Communicate in writing, and speak effectively

- Emotionally stable

- Free from any physical deformity

- Skillful with the assigned departmental firearms

- Good overall intelligence

- Have an elevated level of agility for the job

- Never convicted of a crime

- Pass a physical medical examination

- Pass a psychological examination

- Pass an evasive polygraph examination

ONE MAN'S OPINION

- Posses good physical strength

- Posses people skills

- Possess a High School Diploma or Equivalency

Needed Skills:

- Bilingual

- Microsoft Excel 2000

- Microsoft Outlook

- Microsoft Word 2000

# My Police Philosophy

Thru-out my 26-year career as a police officer, my philosophy always holds me, as well as others, accountable to the highest standard for quality, timely, and cost-effective outcomes and pass it on to my subordinates. Always prepared to meet the demand of customer service, both internal and external, strongly believing in being decisive in keeping myself well informed in making efficient and timely decisions with limited data.

Always keeping an open mind in implementing flexibility for change and striving for added information to adapt rapidly to changing trends.

As a retired Senior Administrative officer with the City of Miami Police Department, I acquired experience in Patrol procedures, Administrations, Communications, Property evidence and confiscation, Community Relations, Community Policing, Prisoner processing and transport, Front Desk Duties, Formalization of emergency Mobilization roster during City Disturbances, and report writing. In addition, I was a former Police supervisor Lieutenant with the Veterans Affairs Police Services in Miami, Florida.

As a former Captain of Operations and Patrol with the Greater Los Angeles area Veterans Affairs Police Services, I experienced the responsibilities of helping run a progressive police

Department similar and comparable to a regular Metropolitan Police Force.

I am a follower of the highest standard in ethics, and my philosophy is to be dependable and display consistency in exercising integrity and honesty when dealing with people. Always leading by example, expecting all staff members to do the same. My experiences as a Police officer throughout my career have shown me the proper way in which to treat others, taking the approach of displaying courtesy and people sensitivity with a high level of respect.

As Chief of Police, one of the most significant needs is to give your staff direct and accurate oral information to filter down to the lower chain of command. Always treat them with respect, courtesy, and honesty, while exhibiting an elevated level of compassion with understanding for your employees to respond with a receptive and cheerful outlook.

All managers and supervisors are analytical people. Always ready and prepared to recognize and analyze problems, considering the relevance, and accuracy of the information, which has been gathered. Always willing to recommend workable solutions to erase existing problems.

As an effective leader, a supervisor must have the resilience to recover quickly from setbacks. Springing back quickly to deal efficiently with ongoing pressure surrounding his work needed while remaining optimistic and persistent under rivals.

While writing memos, letters of commendations, letters of reprimand or dismissal, the Chief, Supervisors, or appointed staff officer must have a well and understood method of written skills in communication to have the employee understand them. The message must be clear, accurate, well-organized, and understandable for the audience to accept it.

Experienced supervisor, both in the local and federal system, I always stressed the importance of encouraging and fostering the right for people to give and express their differences of opinion. Taking steps in implementing taught practice conflict management to prevent counterproductive confrontations concerning hostile incidents involving Police Officers.

Always encouraging police employees to learn how to assess their strengths and weaknesses by acquiring training reflecting on their profession; Suggesting self-development in a continual learning process, which will give them precondition, and the prerequisite needed for achieving higher standards and levels of education during their career.

This encouragement will help employees seek out better ways to perform tasks in a better and shorter time, affording them the opportunity to apply initiative, creativity, and innovation in a progressive way in approaching problems affecting the police service; In addition, reminding them of the value in questioning conventional approaches and encouraging them to look for innovative ideas and innovations. Periodically having supervisory meetings to make them aware of the importance of teaching and to prepare their employees to meet new challenges that lay ahead of them by performing and contributing to the organization.

Giving them the opportunity and a sense of belonging to the organization in helping develop others to offer suggestions and ideas with issues concerning their organization; In addition, reminding Police Supervisors as well as Police personnel of the importance of having a good working relationship with the labor bargaining unions because they are part of the employee's protection process.

# I'd walk a mile for the purpose of living

"I would walk a mile for living" Just like you would eat to live, I walk to live.

Walking is the best exercise anyone can do. It does not take that much effort, and it does not cost anything. A frisky thirty-minute walk a day is healthy for the body. It cleans your plumbing throughout your body and makes the blood travel smoother thru your veins.

It is a fact; a substantial portion of our population is overweight. Not just because of eating too much or because they do not take the time to exercise, the real reason is they are busy working to support their Families.

It is a commitment that an individual must make for the process of good health to take effect. In today's society, people are preoccupied with other insignificant things that they set aside, which is, most importantly, their health.

Taking only thirty minutes a day, four to five times a week, will make people healthier and help bring down blood pressure and sugar levels to a healthy range. A proper diet low in carbohydrates and cutting down on sugar should cause the average person back to a reasonable level of physical fitness. Water consumption is also incredibly significant. After every walk, you should drink an eight-ounce glass of cool water and follow thru with seven more types of grass throughout the day. Keeping hydrated is particularly good for staying healthy and giving a good tone to your skin.

Working up a good sweat causing your sweat glands to filter out the toxin from your body, is essential for good health. Drinking plenty of water while exercising is especially important; it prevents you from getting overheated and getting heat stroke. So, I say to all... Walk, Walk into good health:

# Sample narrative of an "Armed Robbery" incident Report

When a crime has been committed, there should always be the following components and the "RULE" of the five-5 *"W's" and the one -1 *"H" for the Investigation to be successful. These rules apply to all personnel in Law Enforcement when conducting any Investigation.

They are as follows:

1. The Law that was broken or violated.

2. The person committing the violation is the offender.

3. The victim.

4. The place and time of the offense.

5. *Who is it about (Victim)?

6. *What happened (The story)?

7. *When did it take place (Date / Time)?

8. *Where did it take place (Location / Address)?

9. *Why did it happen (Reason)?

10. *How did it happen (Actions)?

In any investigation, there should always be the "RULE" of the (Five- "W's" and the one "H" to arrive at a suitable outcome. (Who,

What, When, Where, Why, How). They do not necessarily have to be in that order. Regardless of the incident, when these elements come together, crime has been committed.

The below Sample narrative covers all four elements, therefore, should be accepted by local, state, and federal Prosecutors to go forth with the case.

(When); On May 29, 2011, at 6"00 PM, (What); I was dispatched to an Armed Robbery, (Where); at 10001 SW Stanley Road (Who); On my arrival, I met a young woman named Rita Smith who told me, (What); she had just been robbed by a young white male in his early twenties. (How) she said that he pointed a white revolver at her and asked for her jewelry. (Why), He took from her one gold watch and a gold chain worth a total of Five hundred dollars ($500.00).

I asked her for a description, and she told me that he was about Five feet – Eight inches tall. He had a neatly trimmed mustache and a small scar on his left cheek. He was wearing a dark blue shirt and light faded blue jeans. She also told me that it had happened approximately ten minutes before my arrival.

I immediately notified the dispatcher to put out a BE ON THE LOOKOUT (BOLO) for the offender to all units in the city. I asked her for any witnesses, and she said none.

I finished my first report and notified Robbery Unit twenty-five, Detective Jones, of the incident and forwarded a copy of the report for further follow-up.

# To the Moon and beyond

Neil Armstrong was the first man to step onto the surface of the Moon on July 21, 1969. About six hundred million people worldwide watched this event unfold before their eyes as they watched their TV sets. There have been six staffed landings (between 1969 and 1972) and numerous unmanned landings. It is time to return to the Moon and beyond.

We have the resources, we have the technology, and we have the resolute personnel to make it happen. So, what is holding us from this accomplishment? Why are we wasting our time and resources on other projects of no importance, such as looking for life in other Worlds? If there is life out there in time, we will know.

## *My hypothesis.*

We have the proper Space Craft, the Shuttle, to perform this task. The Shuttle is big enough to conduct this mission, fly to the Moon, the Planet Mars and beyond. With few adaptations, the Shuttle would be more suitable for longer space flights instead of just orbiting and returning to Earth. Additional Hydrogen tanks can be adapted while the spacecraft docked at the space station for a trip to the Moon and The Planet Mars in a shorter time.

These tanks could be the same size as the ones presently used. Giving it enough fuel does not worry about being stranded in space. Extra fuel would also make it possible for the spacecraft to operate at a faster speed making the time to and from the Moonless. When it arrives at the Moon, it will go into a proper orbit, making any necessary adjustments before the Astronauts descend to the surface.

Other adaptations, such as control nozzles, allow the Shuttle to maneuver while in space. There is a cargo bay space where food, water, and other lifesaving items can be stored for the Astronauts' use during their mission.

The cargo bay is big enough to take a small Lunar Module to the Moon. Once the Shuttle is in orbit, the Module could exit the Shuttle and descends to the surface of the Moon. Allowing the crew to remain on the Moon's surface for longer periods to achieve their scientific analysis.

A total of two men and two women would be enough for the mission to the Moon and Mars.

In departing the Moon orbit, the Shuttle would return to the Space Station where they would disconnect from any unnecessary tanks leaving them at the Space Station, returning to Earth as they have been doing.

With the same number of crew, the same procedure used to go to the Moon could be used to travel to the Planet Mars and back. They could use the same Lunar Module to descend to the surface of

Mars and back to the Shuttle for the trip back to Earth.

The Astronauts would feel safer and more secure in a Space Craft, bigger and more spacious allowing them more room to move around, not making them feel claustrophobic. In a bigger Space Craft, such as the Shuttle, the trip to the planet Mars would be safer by adapting it to automatic computer control to assist the pilot with any minor adjustment during the flight.

Extra fuel tanks adapted to the Shuttle docked at the Space Station would help increase its speed making the trip to Mars shorter. I believe a round trip from Earth to Planet Mar is possible in Six Months. Allowing a week for the Astronauts to go down to Mars's surface to make the analysis needed and back to the Shuttle while in orbit.

Once the Shuttle has achieved the Missions to Mars or the Moon, it returns to the Space Station to make the adjustments for the return trip to Earth. After would undock and return to Earth the same way they have been doing for decades. Phasing out of the Shuttle currently is a big mistake. Please reconsider the phase-out of this Craft.

# Combat Strategies Against the Enemy During War Time Involving Rules Of Engagement

When confronting an enemy with Superior Forces and with the intentions and determination to win, you must counter and be swift and precise in taking the initiative to gain the upper hand. You must do so quickly to be efficient in your mission.

Total gathering of unquestionable Intelligence must be a key part of the enemy's Arm forces if you are to be successful.

Any planned attack should involve the consensus of all the Military branches to work cohesively, synchronizing all tactical maneuvers working together at the same time to be successful.

Rules of engagement must be fluid throughout the battle to protect the general population as much as possible. There will always be casualties in any given battle; however, taking steps to cut the possibility of harming the people is an important part of gaining the approval of the people to get them on your side.

When attacking the enemy, you must make him "Blind and Deaf," do it within the first few hours to deny him the ability to recover and launch an offensive. This can achieve in the following ways:

# ONE MAN'S OPINION

1. Destroying his Power plants, eliminating his Electrical grids. This will prevent him from communication with all his supporting units rendering him blind and deaf.

2. Destroying all his Radar Facilities, preventing him from detecting our Aircraft

3. Destroying the Enemy's Military Air Forces Runways to prevent any Aircraft from getting off the ground. While at the same time destroying all Aircraft parked on the ground or in any Hanger.

4. Land and deploy enough ground troops in and around all Civilian Airports creating a perimeter to take control. This will allow you to land Aircraft to evacuate and bring in troops at will to achieve the Mission of Neutralizing your Enemy.

5. Search and surgically destroy the enemy wherever you find him; if you do not, he will seek, find, and destroy you.

These Actions are simultaneously performed with synchronization to efficiently conduct the mission. Once the country is secure, the flow of humanitarian supplies should start immediately to help the population.

Once this is achieved, a determination to prosecute and bring to justice the people responsible for the unlawful actions in the country.

This will bring stability and order to the people. Government

Officials responsible for atrocities against the people should be taken into custody and held accountable for their actions.

# Mr. President, we have a problem

Future Fictional simulation Scenario in the year 2012:

The year 2009, dated January 20, is a cool crisp January day, and a new president has just been inaugurated and assumed the presidency with a new administration.

The White House:

The president's adviser > "Mr. President, we have a problem; in a few minutes, you will be getting a phone call from the prime minister of Israel."

The President > "what is the problem?" He will advise you, Sir!

His adviser > "the prime minister will advise you on the emergency."

During this time, the president is standing next to his desk in his oval office. With a surprised look on his face, wondering what was going on. The phone rings, the president walks over to his chair, sits down, picks up the phone, greets the prime minister with a polite hello, and begins to listen. His adviser turns around and quickly walks out of the office, closing the door behind him.

Thirty minutes later, the president called his adviser to come into his office.

The President > "I want you to call the Secretary of State, Secretary of Defense, and all Heads of staff personnel from all branches of the Military Services to be here in three hours."

His adviser > "Yes Sir; Right away Sir"

His adviser returns to his office, gets on the telephone, and immediately begins to call every person needed for an emergency meeting.

Three hours later, all the necessary personnel was requested to arrive for the conference. They are all advised to go to the oval office. They all look at one another with surprised looks on their faces, and no one asking why. They all take their proper seating position around a large conference table. The adviser tells everyone the president is on his way. Everyone is waiting nervously to find out why all have been summoned on such short notice.

When the President arrives, everyone stands up. As the president enters the room, he walks over to the head of the conference table and sits down. Everyone then takes their sits.

The President > "Gentlemen, it is now 10:00 AM eastern standard time, and we have a very serious problem; Israel is attacking Iran as we speak, and we all know the ramification arising from this action. However, the prime minister told me that it was necessary because their security and the status of Israel as a nation are at stake. He has asked me if I would be willing to stand by and be ready to act in their defense if needed. I told him our Nation will do whatever is necessary to ensure continuance of the existence of the state of Israel as a free democracy and not allowed to be wiped out by Iran."

The President > "the next twenty-four hours will be the most significant time in our history because the fate of the World is uncertain. However, we cannot aloud Iran or any other country to wage war against Israel. If they do it to Israel, they will do it to us. As a strong nation both economically and militarily, we must exercise our strength if we are to continue to look like a leading nation supporting democracy and insure our own existence."

Twenty-four hours later, the media makes an emergency announcement over the airways: Israel has delivered a message to the leaders of Iran that never again will they inflict fear into the hearts and souls of the Jewish people.

Israel has just attacked Iran, inflicting heavy damage to its nuclear plants, which produce plutonium, destroying all of Iran s nuclear powers. You can still see large plumes of smoke for miles high in the atmosphere across the borders of Turkey, Afghanistan, Iraq, India, and Pakistan. Israel has not attacked any of the major cities, only its nuclear facilities limiting the civilian casualties.

Israel is getting ready to set five hundred-thousand troops on Iran s soil to take over the Capital and take control of the country. Russia has asked the United Nations to intervene and put a stop to what they considered Israeli aggression against a neutral Nation. Russia said that if the UN fails to prevent further destruction by Israel, it would be forced to erase Israel from the face of this Earth. The United States has told the president of Russia not to attack Israel if they do not want to have the same devastation inflicted on them. Russia has yet to respond.

Hundreds of Israeli warplanes are still flying freely over the airways of Iran. They are not being challenged by the Iranian Air force. Iran s Air forces have been neutralized. A report has just come in; they have seen more nuclear explosions near the borders of Iraq and Turkey. The Earth in that area of the world still is shaking from all the bombs dropped.

Hezbollah fighters crossed into Israel and began shooting civilians randomly, creating large numbers of casualties to the civilian population. They see this as an opportunity to create a second front to the war against Israel. Syria is gathering its forces along the Syrian border with Israel, waiting for the right moment to invade Israel.

China has asked for an emergency meeting of all countries to seek an end to this madness, which could end our way of life. It has also placed its three-million-men army and its four-million-reserve force in a high state of alert in the event they must march across Southwest Asia into Israel and put a stop to it...

Russia, China, and Venezuela have all gone on high alert, fearing the United States will launch an attack against them. The World trembles as these events unfold. President Chavez has gone on the airways accusing the United States of provoking this attack by Israel to take control of the Worlds oil supply. He has promised to cut off oil supplies to the US, bring in its economy to chaos. The US has not replied. Chavez further said that he would use the oil as a weapon to bring the US to its knees.

The U.S. intelligence has just detected and advised the president of a fleet of Russian Navy Armada on its way towards Cuba and Venezuela. The United States has asked the Russian president to turn around and not approach the area around Cuba, otherwise; it will suffer untold devastation by nuclear reprisal. France, Germany, and Japan have placed their navy near the coast of Iran to aid in evacuating large numbers of the population trying to flee the devastation occurring in their country.

Pakistan has mobilized its forces along the Pakistani borders with India. India, one of the biggest democracies in the world and allied to the US, has gone into a high state of alert, mobilizing its forces just in case Pakistanis forces march across its border. While at the same time suffering from numerous attacks from unknown terrorist groups against its people.

The US has begun to redeploy all its forces in Iraq and

Afghanistan and has mobilized all the reserve forces if needed for actions. Our Nation is at the highest state of alert it has ever been. Placing our nation in one of the most difficult periods in history.

Forty-eight hours later, Israel has many troops on Iranian soil, taking control of the capital Tehran. Every leader in the country was taken and placed under armed guards for security purposes. The country is under martial law and secured.

Seventy-two hours later, Israel is in control of the country and its borders. It has secured Iran as it has never been before. Iran has asked for an emergency meeting with the United Nations, and Israel has told the UN not to allow for the meeting because it will change nothing. It was too late; they had their chance, and all they did was cause their own destruction. Israel will never have to worry about being wiped out, nor will they ever live in fear again. They will fight to the very end. Israel has destroyed the Hezbollah fighters on its soil and has secured all its borders surrounding their homeland.

President Chavez has asked the Russian President to turn its naval fleet around, fearing the US would retaliate against him. The Russian is not complying and is continuing towards Venezuela and Cuba. This has caused President Chavez to worry because it could be the end of his presidency. There is widespread unrest within the country, and the people throughout the country are having civil demonstrations against his leadership.

The US has mobilized its forces and placed a nuclear submarine's safety net along the eastern part of the Atlantic Ocean and the western part of the US on the Pacific Ocean from the Alaskan peninsula to Baja, California. Canada and Mexico have done the same. The US has asked the Russian President to remove his Naval armada from the Caribbean Ocean, from the Island of Cuba, and it has given the Russian president Forty-eight hours in which to comply. The US will block any naval ship entering or leaving the area. The Aircraft carrier, a fleet of destroyers, and atomic submarines are ready to implement a blockade of the region if they fail to comply with US requests.

Israel has allowed all countries to join forces in aiding in rebuilding Iran's infrastructure and bringing its people back to the standard way of life. The United Nations have recognized Israel as a major country with a nuclear arsenal to deal with any additional future threat which might present itself. Iran has surrendered, asked for mercy for its people, and asked Israel for forgiveness for its blunder, which led to its downfall. Israel, being such a merciful country, has complied and shown remorse for its action. An action, which they felt, was necessary for their survival and was displaying mercy by helping to rebuild the country.

Iran will never again be a Muslim running the country. It will experience democracy with the hope that it flourishes and spreads across the muslin's world. Democracy will prevail, there is no question; People in Iran will still be able to practice their religion as they wish without fear of persecution.

The Cuban Leader Raul Castro asked the United Nations to set up a meeting with US representatives to seek a dialog with the U.S., showing fear of preventing an invasion by the US. He has realized that it is about time the US and Cuba re-establishes diplomatic relations for the benefit of its people. Mr. Raul Castro feels the time for reconciliation has come. We must all get together and seek a better world in which we can all live harmoniously.

The media > president has gone to the United Nations in an emergency meeting, asking the American people to aloud him to withdraw membership from the United Nations. The president said that the UN has outlived its intended purpose and can no longer guarantee the security of Nations.

By allowing rogue Nations such as North Korea, Iran, and Somalia to wage havoc around the world, the UN has shown that it can no longer be effective in its mission. Further, more, the US will no longer contribute any more money in support of their cause because other countries are not contributing. Other countries have failed to live up to their responsibility as contributors and have been delinquent in their financial obligations.

The United States is the only country that has been a major economic contributor supporting the entire Mission, which the UN has undertaken since it was created. All countries see this as an unprecedented request made by the leader of the richest and strongest Nation in the modern world. This request has shocked the entire world sending the stock market to the lowest point it has ever been since record time.

It appears that the US, in cooperation with its allies, is going to establish a global law enforcement organization to Police the world's waterways and airways to ensure the freedom of friendly nations against international outlaws who are infesting our world. Renowned leaders throughout the world are asking the US to take an active role and become the Policeman to ensure the safety of all the people in the world because other countries are intimidated by countries like Russia, China, and Iran.

The world has reached a point in history when the balance of power and survivorship is at stake. History shows the United States of America is a survivor and will fight to the very end to preserve its freedom. Make no mistake; America will always survive regardless of the outcome.

# Coming Home from NAM—1966 to 1967

**American Flag**        **Vietnam Flag**       **Peace**

 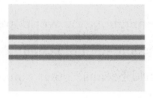 

sign

# ONE MAN'S OPINION

The nineteen sixties were an era of high stress and confusion. Sad and shameful events were taking place during that period; it was supposed to have been the age of innocence, the age of Camelot. We had the youngest president ever elected; his name was John Fitzgerald Kennedy. Born on May 29, 1917, and was only forty-three when he won the election on November 9, 1960. He was 46 years old when he was shot and killed on a Friday afternoon at 12:30 p.m., on November 22, 1963, by a lunatics' bullet whose ideology and twisted mind we will never know. A man with a beautiful family whose dreams for our country will forever remain a dream.

On that Friday, November 22, 1963, my unit was placed on the highest alert our country has ever been since the Cuban incident in October 1962. We were all shocked and surprised on how anyone could be as evil and full of hate to take the life of our president. That same day, I was on a tarmac on an airfield in Fort Campbell, Kentucky, waiting to board C-130s, which were to take us to Texas, but the orders never came.

In nineteen sixty-five, there was an unpopular war waging across a large ocean in a Country few people knew little about. A country that had been at war with France for generations, a country that the United States was trying to bring democracy, became our worst nightmare by getting entangled with its internal affairs and having an unpleasant outcome.

It was a time when there were demonstrations across our Nation, dividing our people. However, it was an era filled with hope, rich with charm and grace, a time of innocence when hippies and the flower people held hands while protesting the war. It was an era of forgiving, an era of caring, an era for showing love for one another. The hippie's philosophy was to love your neighbor without conditions and not meddle in their affairs, especially those of other Countries.

# ONE MAN'S OPINION

It was a time when thousands of young men and women served and sacrificed their lives to protect our way of life. Going across a vast Ocean to help a Country whose people did not appreciate what was being done to protect their nation. While here in our country, our young men, rather than helping our soldiers fighting overseas, were carrying signs protesting the war and running across the Northern Border into Canada to avoid the draft.

A time when family members gathered on weekends to enjoy BBQ parties and discuss a war that was unpopular, causing great despairs among our people while, at the same time, dividing our Nation.

This was supposed to have been the new age of "Camelot" for America. It was a time in our nation's history when it was going through a transition period when everyone was full of doubts about the events taking place in their lives while at the same time filled with hopes. A time when democracy was at its highest and people's rights were evaluated. The war was having a gravely negative impact on our economy, creating high disparity among our younger generation.

It was the time when the Motown Record Company in the City of Detroit had music groups like the Supremes, Otis Redding's, the Impressions, Mamas and the Papas, and many other fine groups, keeping our young people and our country dancing and happy. It was an era of love and warm feelings when everyone found time to care for one another; it was an age of innocence.

In 1960, I was sixteen years old and still in High School. During the school week, I went after three days, Monday, Wednesday, and Friday, after school to do volunteer work at a hospital named Joint Decease, located at 124th and Madison Avenue. I would go to the hospital wards where most of the patients were sick and weakened elderlies and forgotten. I would spend time talking to and reading them stories. At night before leaving, I would show them movies and distribute cookies and apple juice.

On weekends, I worked part-time as a stockroom clerk at a Mama and Papa Pharmacy earning ten dollars a week. Out of those ten dollars, I was able to pay for my mother's washing machine because my father, even thou he was working, was not making enough money to pay for it. In addition, she was not able to pay for it herself. I still had enough money left to take my girlfriend to the movies after work.

Two years from now, I would be of draft age eighteen and join the Marine Corps.

One day while watching TV and seeing the devastation-taking place in Vietnam, I decided to contribute my share of responsibility, as an honorable citizen, by joining the service. Seeing what was happening on TV and watching all those body bags being loaded onto C-130 airplanes, knowing those body bags could have contained friends, was difficult and painful for me to accept.

After attending the funerals of friends with whom I had gone to school, I realized I was not going to sit idle while my friends were coming back in body bags from a war in a foreign land. Seeing these events taking place, I realized it was time for me to go to Vietnam.

By that time, a year had passed, and one day in the middle of May, I grabbed my mother and Father and pulled them aside, telling them I needed to be effective and that I was not going to stand by while my friends died overseas. Both my parents did not like the idea; however, after explaining to them how important it was for me, they understood.

During the school vacation on June 1962, I remember seeing

young kids open Fire Hydrants throughout the city while trying to keep cool during the hot spell. The weather was hot, and there was nothing to do after school. In that same year, on February 9, 1962, I turned eighteen years old, and my friends had already joined the army and had left for Vietnam.

On Wednesday, July 11, 1962, I got up early that morning. I kissed my mother, gave my father a hug, and left to go downtown to the Army recruiting station at Whitehall Street in lower Manhattan to sign up. I first joined the U.S. Marines Corp after finishing with the paperwork; they told me that were they placing me on a thirty-day waiting list. I was not happy with that, so I told the Marine Corps recruiter that I was going across to the Army recruiting station and applied with them.

I then walked across to the Army recruiting station and asked one of the recruiters how long it would take them to process me and have me on my way to Vietnam. They said no time at all; they would do it the same day. After a series of academic battery tests and a physical and psychological evaluation, I took my oath and from that moment, I was a member of the United States Army.

Before I left the recruiter's station, one of the recruiters gave me a Subway token and told me to be at their recruiting station on Friday, July 13, 1962, at 8:00 a.m. in the morning. When Friday finally arrived, I was happy and proud, knowing that I was finally on my way with a group of men that had joined the same day to contribute to a just cause. That day, at 1:00 O'clock p.m., we all climbed onto a Greyhound Bus, which was parked in front of the recruiting station and departed to spend sixteen weeks of Training at Fort Dix, New Jersey Army Training Center.

The trip from lower Manhattan to Fort Dix took two hours. While on the bus, I was able to catch up with my thoughts and think about what the rest of my life was going to be like. I was already missing both my father and Mother, and I just closed my eyes to enjoy the ride until we arrived at Fort Dix. When we arrived at the entrance of the base, it was 3:00 O'clock p.m. It took us about ten minutes from the entrance of the base to the area where the Barracks were located.

When the bus came to a stop in front of the Barracks, and the doors opened, a tall slim white Sergeant walked into the bus and started yelling from the top of his lungs for everyone to exit the bus immediately. I quickly picked up a little carrying bag that my father had bought me and rushed out the door as fast as I could.

When everyone was finally out of the bus and onto the parking lot grounds, he started yelling as loud as he could, telling us he wanted us to make six roles, six men abreast, four roles deep. He told us that he wanted a Platoon formation. In the meantime, another

Sergeant came over and introduced himself as our Platoon Drill Instructor, "DI," for the first phase of our eight weeks of Basic Training.

During this time, he kept us on that parking lot ground for another hour, shouting and yelling at the top of his lungs. He walks between us while still yelling, placing his face right in from of ours. Every word that came out of his mouth had the four-letter "F..." word. He finally came to me and stopped right in front of me, placing his ugly face twelve inches from mine where I got the scent of his nasty, foul smelly Tobacco breath while spiting on my face as he kept yelling and shouting at me. If that was not bad enough, he smelled like the armpit of a thousand Camels.

As he kept shouting at me, I wanted to take him, flipping him on his back so that he would not do that to me again. He then asked me where I was from. Without giving me a chance to reply, he asked me if I was a switchblade knife-carrying Puerto Rican from Brooklyn, which was a stigma placed on our ethnic group by society without any foundation. I had never carried any weapon, let alone a switchblade knife, however; this stigma followed me all throughout my time in the service.

During all this time, the other Sergeant just stood there, not saying anything because the Platoon Sergeant out-ranked him. After enduring an hour of madness under a hot sun in that parking lot, I realized the type of treatment I would be facing every day while at Basic Training. When he finally stopped yelling, he took a deep breath; he walked us to our Barracks, where we could choose any bunk we wanted. When I went in, I picked the first bunk I saw, which was next to the main entrance. Once inside the Barracks, the first thing I noticed was how filthy the Barracks were.

After everyone was inside, he looked around at all of us and told us that we were having a "GI" party. When I asked him what a "GI" party was, he told me that we were going to scrub the Barrack from top to bottom. He then proceeded to show us the utility closet where the cleaning equipment was located, the brooms, the mops, and buckets. He then said to all of us to make sure that the Barrack was squeaky clean; otherwise, we would have to do it all over again until we got it right. At that moment, I looked at my watch, and so did the rest of the men, and saw that we only had about two hours to get the place cleaned up before we could go to the Mess Hall to get Army chow, "Army food."

Two hours later, which was 4:45 p.m., we could see the Sergeant on his way to our Barracks; by that time, we had everything cleaned and looking good. As he entered the Barrack, he immediately asked me to get paper, and a pencil, to follow him as he walked around inspecting and to write down any discrepancy found during the inspection.

As he was walking around, he told us that the place looked

so immaculate that he had never seen it look so clean. He made a comment about the floor; he said that it was so clean and bright that you could see your face. He asked us how we do it, and we told him that we used plenty of floor wax and used a heavy-duty buffer to bring out the shine. He was overly impressed with the results. I never did have the chance to write any discrepancies because he did not find any.

He then told us to go outside for a Platoon formation for a head count so that we could all go after that to eat. We placed all cleaning equipment away in the utility closet, and we all went outside for formation. After the headcount, we made a line, each man side by side at arm's length, to do a police call.

This meant we would all walk around the Barrack side by side and pick up every piece of paper and cigarette bud we could find. He then said in a boisterous voice, "if you people don't do this

right the first time, we will do it repeatedly until the area is spotless."
When the police call was finished, we all marched as a platoon to
the mess hall, singing cadence all the way. After chow, we returned
the Barracks the same way, in a platoon formation and looking like
a professional group. At the end of the day, it was time to relax and
get some rest.

We were all tired from the trip and from the work we had
done when we arrived at the base. I was looking forward to the
following day, which was Friday. The Platoon Sergeants' room was
inside the same Barrack we were housed in. After we had returned
to our Barracks, the Sergeant came out from his room and said for
all of us to get some sleep because we had early reveille at 5:00
O'clock in the morning, and we had to be outside in platoon
formation for roll call. I went into the shower area, took a quick
shower, shaved, and went to sleep.

The next day Friday, we all got up at 5:00 a.m. and went out to make formation; after the headcount, we went for a mile run with the Sergeant in from of us, calling cadence as we ran. We ran for about fifteen minutes, which turned out to be a full mile.

After the run, we got back to the Barracks, where he released us so that we could rush inside, take quick showers, and be back outside for formation to go for breakfast. Afterward, we were outside in formation, ready to march to the mess hall for morning chow. As we marched to the mess hall, I saw the rest of the troops that were in the area also on their way to have chow.

The mess hall was large, housing about two hundred recruits. There were men from all areas of the country, from New York City to California and a few from the Island where I was born, Puerto Rico. For me, not ever having been out of the city, it was a unique experience, also rewarding.

I had the opportunity to meet people from all over and to learn from them. After chow, we went back to the barracks to receive an orientation of the training that was ahead of us. The rest of the day was processing and receiving classes on the rules governing Fort Dix, New Jersey.

Afterward, it was 5:00 p.m., the end of the day, when we had another formation and then released for the weekend. During the weekend, we could not go anywhere because we were new recruits and did not qualify to get a weekend pass. Finding the weekend boring, I and a few of the men decided to walk to a place called the Post Exchange, better known as the "PX," to eat and drink coca cola.

After that, I went back to the barracks to listen to the radio and passed the time away until Monday. I would listen to the latest Motown Hits on the radio with the men and look at the Playboy Magazines, which we found in the Barracks while waiting for the weekend to end.

Finally, it was Monday; we went through the same routine every day of getting up early in the morning for the Physical Training run, "PT," and afterward for the beginning of our eighth week of intensive infantry training. The first eight weeks of phase one of basic Infantry was excruciating enough, but the second phase was just as excruciating.

During the first eight weeks, we received physical training every morning; in addition, we had a physical agility test to determine our strengths and weakness. We received training in marksmanship, both the Army issue M-1 rifle and the Army Colts-45 caliber automatic pistol, hand-to-hand combat, proper patrols procedures, map reading, M-1 Fixed Bayonet training, nighttime patrol training, and survival training while confronting the enemy.

During the marksmanship training, I was able to qualify and receive the rating as an expert with the M-1 rifle. Because of having the ability to fire my weapon accurately and hitting my target bull-eye, my instructors were incredibly pleased with my performance. As a result, they gave me the name "Hindu" because of my accuracy with all the targets placed within my sector. Having this ability to be so accurate, I earned their respect and praise.

As my training continued, I became an expert in all I was taught. Finally, the eight weeks of Basic Training were ending. I graduated on a Friday with high ratings earning respect and friendship of the men in my platoon.

After graduating on that Friday, I went home on a two-week leave to see my family. When I got home, my father and Mother were happy to see me in my crispy starched Khaki uniform. Those were the two happiest weeks I can remember.

Because it gave me the opportunity to talk to my parents and show them that the decision I had made to join the army was the best decision of my life, both my father and Mother were so proud of me that my mother began to cry with pride, and my father kept shaking my hand congratulating me on my accomplishment.

They knew that I only had two weeks and that I would be going back to Fort Dix for the second phase of training. During those two weeks, I got as much rest as I could because, in the end, I would be heading back to Fort Dix for the second phase of training.

The two weeks of leave passed so fast that I could not believe it was over, and it was time to head back again to Fort Dix. I said goodbye to my parents, hugging both and watching their sad faces as I walked out the door heading back to the base. Once again, I found myself on a Bus heading back to Fort Dix, New Jersey, for the remainder of phase two, eight weeks of Advance Infantry heavy weapons Training.

This time, going back to the base was not so hard. I was already familiar with the system and knew how to manage the part of being away from home. In addition, while back at the base, they treated me differently than when I was there the first time.

During the first week of phase two of Advance Infantry training, October 1962, our Drilling Instructors, "DIs," notified us that our president had just ordered a full-scale alert of our armed forces because he was sending the Navy to the coast of Cuba to set up a blockade around the Island. We were all shocked and in disbelief that something so serious could be taking place during the first two years of having the youngest president ever elected.

These were tough times for both the United States and the

Soviet Union. Two of the most powerful countries in the world were close to having a Nuclear Confrontation, which could have, been very destructive to both countries, leading to World War III.

The intelligence provided to President Kennedy by Attorney General Robert F. Kennedy, who was his brother and closest adviser at the time, was one of the most important pieces of intelligence given to any president. It involved the Soviet Union sending and placing nuclear-armed missiles on Cuban soil.

After getting updated verification of the information he had received, President Kennedy made a divisive and unconditional demand to the Russian Premier to remove missiles immediately and turn the ships around, or they would blow them out of the waters.

After seeing that President Kennedy was serious, Premier Khrushchev gave the orders for all Russian Cargo Ships with missiles on their decks to turn around and head back to Russia. It was a crucial time in history when two Superpowers have ever been so close and on the verge of nuclear destruction. It forced both countries to blink and pause, realizing that it was not worth going to war. As far as anyone can remember, it was the only time in history a president was evaluated.

During the second eight weeks of Advanced Infantry Training, I was successful in completing all my classes and training and again achieving high scores on my entire test. At the end of the second phase, during the last week, of training, the head "DI" called me into the company's First Sergeants office to tell me about the test scores I had received during my entry into the service.

He told me due to my high GT scores, which were up in the 130s'; I graduated at the top of my class as a heavy weapons Infantryman specialist. Trained in heavy weapons and trajectory charts plotting involving mathematics equations, which would direct artillery projectiles to our enemy's target. In addition, trained in the use of the 81- millimeter mortar, the heavy 42-millimeter mortar, and the heavy portable 106- Recoilless Rifle and mounted on jeeps. I finally graduated from the eight weeks of Advance Infantry Training and received my orders to report for Airborne training at Fort Benning, Georgia.

After another brief, seven-day military leave, I was on my way to Fort Benning, Georgia, to Amy's special Forces Air Born Training Center, where I received my training as an elite Paratrooper. After graduation from Jump (Paratroopers) school, I went to the elite 101st Airborne Division, "C" Company, 327 Infantry First Battalion First Brigade, better known as the "Screaming Eagles" at Fort Campbell, Kentucky. A Division, formed on July 23, 1918, as part of a parachute and glider regiment during World War II.

## *WW II 101<sup>st</sup> Airborne Glider patch*

The rest of the men I graduated with went to Fort Bragg, North Carolina, the All-American Division. While being assigned to the 101<sup>st</sup> airborne division, I received training from the Armies Airborne Special Rangers in jungle warfare techniques and nighttime escape and evasion, lasting one week. This training was to prepare me for survival if I was ever captured by the enemy during wartime. During the training, I made friends from other parts of the country, and different cultures, giving me a good perspective and knowledge of other people's behavior and the way they think.

Nineteen sixty-three (1963) was a difficult year for me because I was having trouble communicating with my parents. Letters I wrote to my mother, but she never answered. This was a major concern because her writing was always like clockwork; there would be a letter every week, and suddenly, without any reason, her letters stopped coming.

I tried calling her numerous times without any answer. I would try not to think about it because it was having a negative effect on my job performance. This went on for two months, January and February.

Toward the end of February, I was able to contact my sister, who told me that my Father and Mother had separated. I asked her to tell me what had happened, but she refused, telling me that it was our parents' problem and for us not to get involved. I told her that I refused to accept her answer and that I was going to ask for some time off from my company commander to go home and find out the truth.

After that, I went thru the chain of command, first my platoon Sergeant, next the First Sergeant, and finally the company commander. When I was on my way to the Commander's office, the first Sergeant called me over and asked me if I was involved in any sort of problem and if he could be of any help, I told him that it concerned my family back home and that I needed time off to take care of them. He then said, OKAY, see the commander.

I walked down to the commander's office and knocked on his door, and he asked me to come in, closing the door behind me. I stood in front of his desk and saluted him; he returned my solute and asked me to sit down. He asked me how he could help; I began to explain by telling him about the letters I had written to my mother and how I was not getting any response from her. He asked me if I had tried to contact any other member of the family, like a brother, or sister, to see if they knew of any problems our parents were having. I told him yes. He then asked what they said to you. I told him they did not tell me anything.

I then asked him if I could have a thirty-day hardship leave, and he said no. I was so disappointed; I could not speak anymore, and for a moment, I thought I had swallowed my tongue. He then asked me if he could do anything for me else, and I said no. I stood up, saluted him, and walked out the door. As I was walking down the hallway to my room, I encountered the First Sergeant, who asked me how things went with the commander; I told him not good. That he had denied my leave request, he advised me to see the Chaplin and explain my problem to him so that he could find a way to help me. I said, "Okay, I will." I then excused myself and continued to my room.

It was Thursday, seven p.m., night; I was all alone in my room, feeling depressed. I was upset about my commanders' refusal to grant me the leave I had requested. Trying hard to figure out a way I could get home. During that night, as I lay on my bunk, I could not sleep a wink; all sorts of things were running through my mind, including the thought of going "AWOL." I knew that if I did that, it could ruin my record with the army.

The next day Friday, after I was released from duty at 5:00 p.m., at the advice of the First Sergeant, I went to see the Chaplin. I explained my situation to him, how I had gone to see my commander with the request and how he had turned me down. He understood perfectly and told me that he was going to speak with the commander and see if he would change his mind.

Afterward, he would contact me on Monday and let me know his answer. I told him that I was grateful for his help and was looking forward to his response.

When Monday came, as I was walking out of the Barracks, I saw the Chaplin going into the commanders' office. When I returned at the end of the day and entered the Barracks, I noticed that the commander was still in his office. As I was walking down the hallway to my room, while passing his office, he called me and asked to speak with me.

He looked upset, I saluted him, but he did not return my solute. That is when I realized that the Chaplin had spoken to him.

He told me that I was being insubordinate to his command decision by going over his head and seeing the Chaplin. I told him that I did not need his approval to see my Chaplin. He became highly upset and boisterous, yelling at me where; it was heard on the entire first floor. Causing the First Sergeant to come out of his office to see what was happening. He told me that I did not need his approval to see the Chaplin, however; I should have first come back to see him and be more specific about the kind of problem I was having, and he would have reconsidered his decision and granted me the leave.

He then told me to leave his office, restricting me to the Barracks for fifteen days. Before leaving his office, I asked him if he was giving me a military article -15; his response was, "yeas." For the next fifteen days, I was restricted to the Barracks and had "KP" every day for the entire two weeks. After getting through this punishment, the men in the company told me that I could consider myself a Kitchen Police "KP" expert, which I found to be hilarious.

I then went back to see the Chaplin and explained what had happened with the commander because of his coming to see him. The Chaplin was upset and not happy to hear what the commander had done, so he was going back to find out why I was being punished for exercising my rights as a soldier with the U.S. Army. I told the

Chaplin to leave things alone because I had enough problems and did not want anymore. I then left the Chaplain's office and went back to the Barracks.

That same week, I was surprised to receive a letter from my mother; it was four pages long, explaining why she had not written to me. I was happy to hear from her and all she had to say. In her letter, she described the situation she was having with my father and how it was affecting her emotionally as well as physically. She said in her letter that she had reached the point of having a nervous breakdown. Having to leave for a while and stay with one of her sisters to regain her sanity.

For the next few months, things went smoothly; she stayed connected with me by sending me a letter every other week. This woman was my life, who had taken care of me until I was old enough to take care of myself. It was something I needed because being away from home for most people is not pleasant. I began to be more relaxed and tentative about the things that were going on around something, which I had lost for a while. During the next couple of months, we had a change of Company Commander, which was music to my ears. Knowing that he was gone was the best news one could have had.

The following year, in nineteen sixty-four (1964), my unit participated in training missions all over the country. Before any mission, the entire 101st Airborne Division 1st Brigade would have an Inspectors General Inspection (IG) by General William Westmoreland, who was our Division Commander at the time to determine the readiness status of all three Brigades.

Our company was having ours in November of that same year on a Friday when the weather was nice and cool. During the inspections, my platoon leader inspected me in my Army Green dress uniform. He also inspected all my field duty equipment. When the inspection was over, the company commander told all the platoon leaders to choose the man who had passed the inspection with the highest ratings in their platoon. During an inspection, one of the other Squad leaders from another platoon showed some of the men my field gear layout and told them how a field gear layout should look like.

After inspection, we all went outside in front of the Barracks, to hear our Company Commander talk to us and congratulate us on our accomplishment. After the formation, they released us to return to the barracks. I was one of man who passed inspection with the highest ratings; as a result, my platoon leader gave me a weekend pass. That Friday, I left for Nashville, Tennessee, to enjoy my weekend pass.

At the end of November that year, in 1964, I went to California's Mohave Desert for Desert Warfare training. The mission was "Desert Strike," involving numerous Divisions and

Special Forces. I was there for a Month; during that time, even thou the rest of the country was having wintry weather, the temperature in the desert during the day was about 135 degrees. It got so hot you could fry eggs on top of the hood of our jeeps. However, at night, it got so cold and damp to the freezing point when we had to wear a field Jacket to keep us warm. To make matters worse, the month we were there it rained several times which was unusual for that time of the year, making it more miserable.

During one of those hot days in the desert, most of the men in my platoon were tired and to the point of dehydration. We tried to make a shaded cover with our ponchos, issued to us as rain gear to protect us from the hot Sun; otherwise, it would have been unbearable. Even with the covers during the day and the suntan lotions we used, we were still Sun- burned to the point that we looked like dark chocolate Hershey bars.

# ONE MAN'S OPINION

One day we all decided to take our boots off to rest our feet. When a Special Forces Sergeant from another unit happened to be walking by, and approached us and told us to be careful with the hot sand because we could get burned and develop blisters on our feet, which would cause infections. The man and I made it a point to keep that advice in mind.

During the weekends, as the sun went down and became cooler, some of the men would hang around their tent area, play cards, and just talk about anything that came to their minds. I would take walks with some of my bodies into the surrounding hills looking to see what we could find. While walking around the hills between large boulders and rocks, we came across vast areas blanketed by a beautiful layer of green grass with lots of little black burrows.

Unknown to us, those little burrows contained Tarantula

spiders that were ugly and hairy. As we continued walking throwout the area, we began to see them come out and stay by the entrance of their burrows. They were large, Black hairy tarantula spiders with leg spans as big as my hand, about six inches across. I asked my body, how can a spider so large crawl into such a little hole? In seeing this, we turned smartly around and left the area. We did not want to have anything to do with such ugly and hairy critters. Even thou they are not poisoners, they can still give you a nasty bite, which would be painful.

As we continued walking out of the area, we also came across Desert rattlesnakes causing us to be concerned. Because while looking for a warm place to hide and sleep at night, one could easily crawl into our tents, biting one of us. Even thou the Deserts are beautiful and serene, they are extremely dangerous places to find yourself in.

# ONE MAN'S OPINION

One of the most memorable things I remember while being in the Desert was the nighttime sky. On a clear night, you can see forever. In addition, at night, the jeep's hood was cooler, and I would lie down looking up at the sky and seeing millions of stars blinking like fireflies.

Every night I would find myself with some of my body just staring up to the sky at what appeared to be an eternity and appreciating the beauty God has given us.

At the end of the day, we used our downtime to clean all our equipment, such as our weapons, our jeeps, the heavy-duty trucks, and personnel carriers, which would be full of sand, making them more prone not to function properly. I also made sure; we did not have anything-nasty crawl into our sleeping bags or our boots. In the morning, when I got up, I would pick up my sleeping bag and shake the hell out of it to make sure it was clear from any unwelcome visitors of the night. I did not want to become a victim of one of those critters. If you were bitten by a rattlesnake, the chances were if you did not receive treatment immediately, you would most likely die, or they can put you out of commission by sending you to a hospital for a month.

Finally, after being there for a month, it was time to leave the desert and return to Campbell, Kentucky. When we returned to Fort Campbell, we unpacked our equipment and began to clean it up. We all went back to our normal ways of getting up at 4:30 a.m. every morning for a five miles Physical Fitness Run. After the run, we took a quick shower and got dressed for breakfast.

From that moment on, we work, bud off until 5:00 O'clock in the afternoon. When it was the end of the day, everyone looked forward to returning to our Barracks. I always looked forward to the end of the week because my friend and I would get our weekend pass, and we would take off to Nashville, Tennessee, to rest and recuperate. Before we noticed it, the weekend was over, and it was time to return to the base and back to the same rat race.

After returning to base, the next day, I went to the first Sergeants office to check the duty roster only to find my name for mess hall detail the following day. A duty known as Kitchen Police, "KP" is a duty that involves scrubbing dirty pots and pans that were big and heavy. Not to mention, use hot soapy water with a large, heavy mop to scrub the floor of the Mess Hall and then dry it up; afterward, wax the floors until you can see your face in it.

The Mess Hall Sergeant always inspected the pots and pans for cleanliness, and if they did not pass inspection, I would have "KP" Kitchen Police working at the Mess Hall for the rest of the week as punishment.

The most hateful thing about "KP" was when the Sergeant had me scrub and clean the Grease pit, which was a real messy and dirty job. A job nobody wanted but a job everybody who had "KP" had to do. Doing an excellent job at "KP" and keeping the Mess Hall clean prevented the Sergeant from having to fail inspection, which prevented me from having the detail for the rest of the month.

After being back for several months and having to get back to duty, I felt my feet getting swollen and itchy; it felt as if I had things crawling inside my skin. It was a miserable feeling because it kept me up at night and caused me to lose sleep.

While in the barracks, I went to my platoon Sergeants room to ask him if I could go on sick call the next day. The Sergeant asked me, "why," I would tell him because of the problem with my feet. He said, "Yes."

On the next day, I went on a sick call and saw the Doctor. While examining me and scraping samples of skin from my feet, he was able to identify the problem. He told me that I had picked up some sort of fungus infection while being in the desert in California. He told me that was the reason for the blister, and if not treated properly with an antibiotic, they could become infected. He also noticed that I had difficulty walking and suggested that I should be admitted to the hospital, which he did, and that would get me off my feet for a while so that he could treat me with antibiotics to get rid of the infection before it got worse.

I immediately called my Platoon Sergeant by phone and explained my situation. He told me not to worry, to go ahead and do whatever needed to be done to get better so that he would come by when he had the chance to see me.

After that, I spent one month in a large hospital bay area, all alone by myself, with no one to talk with. Every morning this nice-looking Nurse would come into the bay area and give me treatment. She would have me sit on a chair in front of a small medical whirlpool tank with both feet inside. She would then fill this whirlpool tank with hot soapy water with a white medicate soap, which would eventually kill the bacteria.

I would spend two hours sitting there watching these soapy waters spin around with the hope that it would get rid of what I had. Afterward, she would help me get back on my feet, help me up to my bed where she would have both of my feet raised up, and strap me to slings holding both legs up about a foot from the bed to prevent them from swelling.

This went on for about a month to the point that I started feeling depressed and resentful towards the treatment I was getting. Can you imagine being in a hospital bay area where there was no

TV or Radio to keep me occupied? Believe me, I was going out of my mind.

After being in the hospital for so long and seeing that I was getting better, I asked the Doctor to let me return to the Barracks where I could continue my treatment; otherwise, I would go crazy. He said no problem, so he prepared the necessary paperwork for discharge.

He told me that the Nurse who was giving me the treatments would be Cumming back with the necessary paperwork for me to sign and give me some medication to take with me, which would help my feet heal.

At the advice of the Doctor, the Nurse returned and walked into the bay area, and she came over to my bed where I was sitting and asked me to get into a wheelchair she had brought for me to take me to the front entrance of the hospital where my platoon Sergeant was waiting to pick me up.

She wheeled me to the front of the hospital, where I saw the Sergeant waiting, who helped me into his vehicle and drove me to the Barracks. I left the hospital with medication to use daily until the infection was gone. The Doctor then told me to return a week later after I felt that I could walk again. A week later, I returned to the hospital, where he checked me out and gave me the all-clear to return to full duty.

I recovered from the infection, and when I saw him again, he told me to make sure to be careful where I placed my feet again. That's when I remembered what the Special Forces Sergeant had said to me while I was in the Desert. During the time I was recovering from the problem with my feet, I would spend days in the Barracks playing cards and watching TV of the events taking place in Vietnam and around the World. The media, by way of TV, brought into our living rooms all the sad things that were taking place, not just in Vietnam but also in other places around the globe. Giving us a front spectator's seat about everything that was happening across a vast ocean as it happened in real life…

It was not only the young people concerned about the things taking place in America but also the older generation, as well. During these tough times, I kept myself busy in the Barracks, cleaning my assigned weapon, an M-16, given to us for the deployment to Vietnam and all the other equipment needed while trying not to think about the deployment.

One morning in 1964, my Company Commander called me into his office asking to speak with me. He told me that he was going over my military records and that he was impressed with what he had seen. I asked him what he meant, and he said that the series of battery tests I had taken during my enlistment was particularly good and above average. That it would be a waste of time if I stayed in the infantry when I could seek out higher levels of training, placing me in a much better position for better jobs after I got out of the service.

He then asked me how I would like it if he was to send me away to school to receive training in Electronics Radar Repair, Ground Control Radar Repair, and Anti-Personnel Radar Repair at Fort Monmouth, New Jersey. He told me that those were the most critical Military Occupational Specialties (MOSs) in the Armed Forces. He felt that I had high potential and that being Infantryman was not appropriate for me. He told me that the training would last twenty-nine (29) weeks, one of the longest schools in the U.S. Army.

The following week I was on my way to the Electronics

Academy at Fort Monmouth, New Jersey, for training. During the training, I realized that what the Company Commander had told me was right. It appears that what he was doing was looking out for me because I had shown him that I was a good soldier.

The training was priceless because I could use it when I was out of the service. Giving me a specialty that a lot of Veterans just coming out of the services would not have. Allowing me the opportunity and giving the advantage over the rest of the Veterans returning home from Vietnam. He also mentioned that I would have to cut my first enlistment short and re-enlist again for me to get the spot on the training roster. I re-enlisted for another tour and left for the Academy for training.

When I returned from school, the Company Commander was glad to see me. He asked me into his office to congratulate me on my accomplishment and invited me to join him for lunch at the

Officer's Mess Hall. I accepted and said thanks. During lunch, he mentioned the possibility for me to attend Officers Candidate School (OCS). I told him that I was not interested because I was not making the army a career. He then said that he had me assigned to Campbell's Aviation Battalion Airfield as a Radar Technician setting Radar Equipment on weekends, making sure that it was operational in the event we had to deploy to Vietnam. At the same time, while at the airfield, I could do Air Traffic Controller duties. My response "was yes. I would, and then I said thank you for all your help." He said, "Do not mention it."


One Sunday afternoon at about 6:00 p.m. on March 1966, I was at the rear of the Headquarters Barracks sparding with my Korean Sansei friend while practicing my Taekwondo martial arts; He was a ten-degree black belt holder, who taught me everything I knew about Korean martial style of fighting. During one of the sparding sessions, while I was preparing for my first black belt degree, as I blocked a high kick aimed at the left side of my head, the kick broke my left arm at the wrist. This incident placed me on the disabled roster for a month. Afterward, I recovered and was good as new, and he awarded me my first-degree Black Belt.

In that same month, my platoon Sergeant came over to me and gave me the news. He told me that I was going to join the rest of the First Brigade that was already in Vietnam and that I had to start getting ready for deployment by the end of the month.

He said that I needed to go to personnel to start processing and receive a series of vaccination needed before deployment. The next day, I went to personnel and received a bunch of paperwork, which I filled out and went, and got my vaccination needed for deployment.

The week came and went, and I finally found myself with a large group of troopers, G I's ready to go to Campbell Airfield to board a large C-130, one of the largest cargo planes at the time. This cargo plane will take us to Saigon, Vietnam. This was the same plane I had jumped from numerous times while at Campbell during days and nights training.

We got to the airfield and boarded the plane with all the gear needed for overseas; inside, the plane was crowded, stuffy, and smelly, making it almost impossible to breathe. We left Campbell Airfield on the afternoon of July 1966; it took us Sixteen hours before we arrived at Bien Hoa Air Base at the Republic of South Vietnam Airport in Saigon.

When we arrived in Vietnam, the weather was hot and humid. I was drenched with sweat so was my uniform, with no relief in sight. As if that was not bad enough, it was raining. We deplaned and had a formation on the airfield tarmac for a roll call while it was still pouring rain.

After everyone was accounted for, we picked up our wet gear and got on a large Army truck for the trip to our destination, the rear area that was the main base camp of the brigade. If there are no incidents along the way, it should take about an hour.

We were going to an area known as the rear area, where most of the Brigade had been set up since their arrival in 1965. After arriving at the rear area, we started processing through personnel; the clerk checked each one of us for the correct paperwork and the proper equipment and assigned us to our tents. When I finished processing, I picked up my wet gear and went to my assigned tent.

After resting for three hours, a platoon Sergeant walked into our tent and asked us to follow him to the mess hall to get something to eat. We were glad that we were going to get something to eat. All of us were hungry because of not having anything to eat, but cold sea-rations were given to us by the flight crew during the flight.

After eating sea-rations for such a long time during the flight, we were glad to know that we were going to have a fresh hot meal to settle our hunger. I told the Sergeant, "If the enemy does not kill us, the bad case of diarrhea from eating all that sea rations will." He almost died of laughter.

After the nice hot meal, we all went to our tens to lay down on our bunks and rest. A few hours later, the "CQ," Charge of Quarters,' walked into our tent asking us to walk across the field from our ten to the reception tent because a Chief Warrant Officer was going to give us an in-country orientation familiarization about the country's laws and customs, which was mandatory for all new recruits. We learned about parts of the country that we could go to and not go to because of safety concerns. The orientation lasted for an hour.

He gave us maps showing the Cities throughout South Vietnam and their locations. He also alerted us about the areas that we must never go to. However, if we did, never go alone; always make sure you have someone with you. After that, we all went back to our tent to get some sleep and be ready for the next day.

The following day, our assigned platoon Sergeant woke us up at five O'clock (5:00 a.m.) in the morning. Our Platoon Sergeant turned out to be a large, humongous person who weights about two hundred and fifty pounds. This Sergeant was huge and as tall as an Island palm tree, with a strong voice of authority.

He told us to get up and get ready to get breakfast because we were shipping out to the forward area in an hour. I did not know what he meant by the forward area. Being curious, I asked, "what are the forward areas, Sergeant," that's when he told us, "That's where all the action is and where you separated the man from the boys." We all looked at each other puzzled about what he had just said, but when he saw our faces, he explained to us what the forward area was.

He told us that the rear area was the place where the enemy would come knocking at our tent door each night looking for a fight and that we had better be prepared to confront him on his own terms; otherwise, we would all be dead by morning.

The statement made by the Sergeant sent cold chills down my spine. What he meant, with the stamen, was that the Vietcong would only be just yards away from our ten at any given time. In addition, we would not be able to see him unless he wanted us to, having an advantage over us in this war. The enemy also wanted to remind us that this was his territory and that he was the expert in his terrain.

# ONE MAN'S OPINION

The Vietcong knew that we would leave just as the French did in 1954 when they occupied their country, leaving the country with their tails between their legs. That is exactly what we did in 1975; we left with our tails between our legs.

A superpower with all our sophisticated weapons, modern technology, and the best-trained soldiers in the World, they were still able to drive us out of their country by having strong tenacity and determination.

During that day, they divided us into diverse groups, and we went to different areas. Some went to Phan Rang, others went to Cam Ranh Bay, and they sent me to the Highlands in the Kontum Province near the Cambodian Border, not too far from the Ho-Chi-Minh trail. They attached me to a small Special Forces unit whose assignment was to train the Montagnard Tribesmen in the use of modern weapons and the art of ambush. Our missions were not engaging the enemy, only observing and keeping track of the Vietcong crossing the borders of Cambodia and Laos into South Vietnam. This area was where the Ho-Chi-Minh trail ran along the border, which divided South Vietnam from Cambodia and Laos, making it easy for the enemy to infiltrate their resupplies.

The job was a difficult one, especially when the communication was limited because they did not speak our language, and we did not speak theirs. In addition, the interpreters assigned to us were tribe members who had difficulty speaking their own language because of different dialects.

Half the time, they did not know what we were telling them to relay to their own people, making things harder. Despite the difficulty we had with them, they were still particularly good fighters, and they fought fiercely without any hesitation against their enemy, the Vietcong. They were also very accommodating with us by letting our small group live within the confines of their small village.

We all went out and cleared an area around the entire village a hundred yards, about the size of a football field, known as a Fire zone. An area where we could see the field and anyone trying to walk or sneak across. The reason for the clearing of the area was that it gave us ample time to respond to any attack during the day or night.

The area was well set up with booby traps and Constantine wire, soda and beer cans, and flairs with sensors that would go off when anyone got near or tripped them. We took a lot of precautions to make sure we had enough warning against any intruders, especially at night when it got so dark you could not see your hand in front of you. We also had Claymore mines deploy spread apart, which would blow up if detonated when anyone tried walking across the field. Being out in the boonies at night was the worst thing that could happen to anyone, including "Charlie," the "VC."

There were nights while pulling guard duty at a perimeter post with my M-60 and ready for the worst when it got so dark I could not even see my hand in front of me; that was very scary. Those nights were most unpleasant for me, while other nights were quiet, and all you could hear was the crickets and the sound of the wind blowing, giving me a false sense of security.

***Pulling guard duty with my M-60 Machinegun and my M-16 by my side on December 24, 1966, the day before Christmas. In front of my position with a clear view of a safety fire zone one hundred yards***

On other nights, I could hear the rattling of the Cans, not knowing whether Charlie had infiltrated our perimeter or was it a poor animal looking for something to eat and subsequently blowing itself up. In addition, on other nights, the area would light up like a thousand candles where; you could see everything in from of you, giving us a clear view of the kill zone in which to take the enemy down.

Other times during the day, it was quiet and with little activity. Giving us downtime for my bodies to relax, play cards, and cut each other's hair. That went on for several months before they flew me out of the area and back into civilization. Boy, was I happy to see that happened...

Due to my Military Occupational Specialties (MOSs), I spent several months going to different areas throughout South Vietnam. Because of my expertise, there were times they sent me to the rear area to help with their communications equipment at Headquarters Company. These times were important to me because they gave me a chance to refresh myself and clear my head. Knowing that I would eventually go right back to the Highlands of

# ONE MAN'S OPINION

Kontum Province to join my detachment at a small firebase.

## *During nighttime patrols near the Cambodian Border in November 1966*

My most tough times were when I was out in the bush the (Jungle) on patrol with my platoon while separated and not being able to see each other because of the dense Jungle until Cumming to opened fields, free from foliate.

The platoon would have few tribe members during patrol because they had an instinct for smelling Charlie when we could not; we all knew that at any time, the Vietcong could attack us, causing casualties. Our detachment was small in numbers having our ability to suppress a large force of Vietcong almost impossible.

There were times the people we trained wanted to go home for the night to be with their families. They thought that they were part-time soldiers and that they could go home at the end of the day. This was one of the problems we had to deal with every day, and as time went on, becoming problematic with no end in sight.

Most of the time, the trainees were cooperative and willing to endure hardship caused by the training; other times, they found it difficult and hard. We were fortunate in the area we were at because the enemy tried to keep us clear from contacting us due to the area being so close to the border; they did not want us to know that they were there.

The HO-Chi-Minh trail, which was in Cambodian bordering, Vietnam, was one of their main travel routes to get their weapons resupplied. They would cross over to the other side where the Ho-Chi-Minh trail was located, giving them haven and safety without fear of being confronted by our troops. The Air force would saturate the area every day with a defoliate substance known as Agent Orange. Striping the trees and plants of their leaves, leaving behind an area that resembles a waist land looking like frozen skeletons in a desert. There were times I would wake up in the morning drenched with the chemical, having to take my uniform off and bury it to prevent contaminating the rest of my clothing. This was an everyday problem I had to deal with.

Our unit had many narrow escapes from the enemy,

especially at night, which was the time that they were supreme because they were accustomed to the terrain and were good night fighters. The Vietcong was the ultimate soldier in dealing with jungle warfare because they had many years of experience.

***One time during the daytime when I was the point men during a patrol walking across an open field of elephant grass while looking out for booby traps with the rest of the platoon in the far background in the rear by the tree lines where you could not see them.***

They knew their tactics, and they knew it well. Furthermore, they were very resourceful with whatever weapon they got their hands on. The Chinese AK-47, an extremely reliable weapon, was their preferred weapon. The weapon that they used fighting the French, they used against us. When they were fighting the French, they learned how to stand up to a higher Power, giving them the experience and expertise to fight a well-trained soldier of the United States.

# REINALDO IRIZARRY

## *On daytime, patrol in Kontum Province in the Republic of South Vietnam, November 1966*

During this period, it was the beginning of December in 1966 when the Christmas holidays; were just around the corner. The Vietcong (Charley), as we called him, knew how important the holidays were for the U.S. soldiers. He was also aware from intelligence that when whenever a holiday came around, every (GI) would get happy and tipsy during the partying and the drinking. Sometimes forget the reason for being there and let their guard down.

Knowing this, the Vietcong used it to their advantage while waiting patiently, knowing time was on his side. That's when he could take advantage of the conditions when our soldiers would find themselves relaxing and lunch an attack.

Our platoon leader put out the word to our entire group for everyone to be alert and to monitor the radios for any activities in our area. These people were smart; you must give them plenty of credit for being so resourceful and cunning. They may be small people in stature but big in self-confidence. These Vietcong people were so cunning that they forced the French out in one of the most successful assaults against the French army at Dien Bien Phu in 1954.

To our surprise, the Christmas holidays came and went with only a brief encounter with the enemy while trying unsuccessfully to penetrate our perimeter. When we went out the following day to scout the area only to find dead bodies all over the place, they were blown to pieces and spread out so far apart that you could not recognize they were human beings. Even today, I still think about these events, and it still brings tears to my eyes because they were still human beings fighting for what they believed to be a just cause for them.

At the beginning of January 1967, my platoon leader told me

that he had received word from the first Sergeant to get me ready because I was to evacuate to the Headquarters Company at the rear because the end of my tour was growing near.

By this time, in February, I was a short-timer; and on my way to the rear area stopping in Pleiku, and Cu-Chi, a small town where I was able to take a few photos and have a few coca kola drinks with some of the people of the town while continuing to several other small towns. In no time at all, I will be going home. I will try to forget about the VCs, the hot, humid weather, and the loud noise pounding of artillery shells. In addition, I the smell of the countryside and the misery I had gone through because I wanted to do the right thing by serving my country and doing my part as a good citizen.

Now that I was back at the rear area, Headquarters Company, I was pulling guard duty and getting all my paperwork ready to get back to the States. While in the rear area, inside my tent, on the first week of March 1967, I was looking at a few photos an Army photographer had taken of me while in the field. Looking at them and then looked in the mirror, noticing and wondering how much I had aged while being in the bush.

I still remember the first Sergeant calling me into his tent and telling me that I would be flying back to the U.S. by way of a commercial Airline. I would be leaving on March 16, flying to Fort Lewis, Washington arriving Sunday Morning, March 18, 1967, to process and be discharged the same day, where I would then receive all the necessary documents needed for my personal military records and my final paycheck. That was the best news any ("GI") could have ever heard.

When March 16 came, they placed me and other soldiers on a bus and drove us to the Saigon Airport, where I boarded a commercial airline and began my long-awaited trip back to the states. Fifteen and a half hours later, I was in the continental United States. Upon arriving in the United States, I got off the plane and went out in front of the terminal to catch a bus.

As I looked around, I saw a bus waiting to go back to Fort Lewis Washington Base. I boarded the bus, which took me to the base, and it dropped me off right in from of the personnel office where I would be processing out of the service.

On Sunday, Morning March 18, 1967, was a cold and damp, cloudy day. I returned that day from the war in the Republic of South Vietnam. The weather was 36 degrees Fahrenheit; it was so cold it felt like cold steel blades going thru me. After being in a country, which was extremely hot most of the time, and humid, I found it shocking to return to a cold place. That day I felt strange; I felt out of place, and I was cold, lonely, and scared.

I was coming home to the country, which was much different from the one I had left behind. There were no marching Bands or loved ones waiting to greet me at the Airport. Instead, people shouted nasty remarks and called me a "Baby Killer" while showing their frustration and disapproval of the war that no one wanted.

It was a dreadful day in my life, making me feel as if everyone had abandoned me. I kept asking myself repeatedly while sitting at the Airport waiting for my flight back home to New York City, was it all worth it… serving my country and receiving such a nasty, unappreciated reception from my fellow compatriots. While sitting at the Airport, waiting for my flight, I could not help but watch people walk by, looking at me as if I were some sort of person from another planet.

While I was sitting quietly in a seat at the terminal near the gate, waiting for my flight, I saw some of the other GIs whose families came to greet them. I could see their response when they saw their loved ones and the joy it brought them. At that moment, I had to turn my head and look the other way because I felt as if I was going to lose my mind. For me, it seemed like an eternity, as if time had stood still.

There was other GIs walking across the terminal with their head looking down, trying not to make eye contact with the rest of the other people around them. I could see that I was not the only one with the problem; there were others. I can truly imagine how they must have felt coming home, the same way I did, with no one to greet them or give them a hug.

Knowing I had several hours before my flight arrived, I got up from my seat, grabbed my duffel bag, and went into the men's bathroom to freshen up, throw water on my face, and change my clothes. I changed from my uniform to civilian clothes; I put on a heavy flight jacket I had brought back from Vietnam to keep me warm. I took my uniform, placed it back into my duffel bag, placed it into a wall locker that they have at the Airports, closed the locker door, locked it, and threw the key into the trash can.

If they have not altered that Airport since March of 1967, that duffel bag must still be the one today. I then went to another area where I would not be seen as a Vietnam Vet, picked up a magazine, buried my head in it to read, and sat down to wait for my flight. From that moment, no one bothered me the rest of the time I was waiting.

After several hours of waiting for my flight, it finally arrived on schedule; I finally was able to board the plane back to New York City. During the flight, I got a seat next to a window where I was able to look out and see the clouds as we departed. I could not help but think and remember the long flight lasting Fifth teen hours and thirty minutes (15- Hrs, 30-Min) I had endured from Saigon, Vietnam, to Seattle, Washington. Then another Six hours flight from Washington to New York City.

When I finally arrived at Kennedy Airport, I took a taxicab into the city, costing me $25.00 dollars; on arrival at my home, I gave the cab driver a $5.00 dollar tip. When I got out of the cab, I took a few steps; I then stopped and took a deep breath-taking advantage of the fresh air. Besides, the weather was not too cold. I looked around for a minute just to get the feel of the neighborhood again. Only to find that everything looked different.

As I walked towards the building where my father was living, the area looked old and dilapidated, as if there were no one taking care of the property. I walked into the building, and it smelled rancid and needed cleaning.

The floor was wet, dirty, and full of beer cans scattered all over the place. It looked like someone had a party the day before and forgot to clean up afterward. I walked towards the elevator to find out that it was not working, so I decided to walk up the stairs; it was only one flight up to the second floor.

I knocked on my father's front door, and this middle-aged woman opened the door and asked me who I was. I told her who I was, and I asked for my father; she then asked me to come in.

As I went into the kitchen, I found my father drunk out of his mind sitting with an empty whisky bottle passed out on the kitchen table. I was so disappointed and shocked that I could not find words to express my feelings.

My father was so drunk; I had to pick him up, take him to his room, take his clothes off and place him in bed. I could not help stopping for a second before walking out of the room and back to look at him to make sure he was okay, hoping that he would recover from a bad hangover the next day. I then asked politely his woman friend to leave and never return.

It appeared that for the four and a half years I was gone, my father had aged quite a bit. When I left for Vietnam, he looked young and healthy; now that I have returned, he looks so skinny and fragile from neglect that I hardly recognize him.

After the woman left, I stood looking out the kitchen window, wondering where my mother could be. I must have stood by that window for an hour with tears running down my cheeks, thinking of all the problems my mother and Father must have been going through while I was away witch, which I was not aware of.

I then walked over to the front door and made sure the door

was locked. Putting the lights out, I walked over to one of the rooms I used to sleep in before I had gone overseas. The room looked different from when I had left it, and even the apartment looked different. I then took off my clothes, off, went over to the bathroom, took a shower, and went to sleep.

The following day was a Monday, March 19. I got up early in the morning, walked over to the kitchen and prepared a cup of coffee with toast and butter and sat down at the kitchen table to eat. After that, I washed the coffee cup, cleaned the table, and went over to my father's bedroom to check on him to see if he was okay.

After seeing all was well, I left the room and walked out of the apartment, locking the door behind me. I then took the stairs down because the elevators were still not working, and out of the building to take a walk around the neighborhood.

# ONE MAN'S OPINION

As I walked and looked around, I reminisced about the days before I had left. While walking around the neighborhood, I noticed that everyone I had left behind was gone. Most of the people in the neighborhood were complete strangers, people I did not know. All my friends had either moved away or joined the army. What I had left behind was no longer there, just memories of what once was.

With no one to talk to, I found myself lonely and full of anger for coming home to an empty, lifeless setting and finding my father, who was my best friend and mentor, in such a sad condition. I felt like a total stranger, not recognizing the people I had left behind.

I must have walked for hours because I went to areas I used to hang out with my friends and found the area dilapidated and old looking. I saw graffiti on the building walls around the neighborhood. I found one of the schools I had gone to close because the city was having a budgetary crisis and had no money.

When I returned from the walk, I found my old man in the kitchen trying to prepare something to eat. I asked him, "Can I help? "and he said no. I sat down at the kitchen table to watch him as he prepared a sandwich. He asked me if I wanted one, and I said, "No, I had already prepared my own breakfast before I had gone for a walk."

I continued to look at him and wonder curiously about the man I had left behind alongside a wonderful woman who was my mother. After having a brief conversation, he finished his sandwich, took one look at me and, without saying anything else, walked out of the kitchen. I just sat there for a moment, shaking my head, not making too much of it while trying to put it out of my mind.

To think, I almost started to ask him about what happened to my mother, his wife, but I hesitated and kept quiet, not saying anything to prevent an argument. The day went on just like any other day, with nothing significant going on. On that day, I told myself I was going to take one day at a time. I was not going to rush into anything before exploring it carefully, and I was not going to let my father's problems get the best of me.

The next day, Tuesday, March 20, I got up and sat by my bed, taking a moment to recover from the shock of coming home to a new setting and start facing reality; I was no longer in a War zone. I had to learn to adjust to the new life that was ahead of me and forget about the war and the friends I left behind. Thou I could not help myself from feeling guilty because I was home in one piece while GIs and friends left behind in body bags.

Those who came home, just as I did, were facing the same stigma that I was experiencing. When I returned, I was an old War hog and a Veteran of a Foreign War, giving me a chance to meet new friends and find a job to help my father with his bills; Bills he had accumulated while I was away because of his neglect.

After the first week of being back from overseas and walking around the neighborhood, I decide to stay home and get some long-earned rest. Telling my old man not to wake me up unless it was an emergency; otherwise, let me sleep, sleep. sleep, He said, "no problem, Son, you go ahead and get all the sleep you need because you earned it." It felt good to hear my dad say Son again because it had been a long time since I had heard him say it.

While in Vietnam, there was no time to rest. It was gone, go, go while always keeping your antennas up, making sure of everything that was going around. That was the only way you were going to come home in one piece. Back home, I spent the entire week getting up in the morning, taking a shower, eating breakfast and going right back to bed. I must have slept a full week; that's how tired I was.

After that week, I would get up in the morning and make my own breakfast because my old man was feeling lazy and would not talk to me. I attempted to start a conversation many times with no results. His reason was that my mother was not there, I knew he loved her very much, and he missed her terribly.

This went on for several weeks, and during that time, I began to go out to look for a job. On Tuesday, April 4, 1967, at the advice of a person whom I had met during the first and second week, I arrived home. He gave me the address to a hospital known as Metropolitan Medical Center, which was located at 96th, and Second Avenue in Manhattan. I took the bus on Second Avenue to 96th; I got off and went across to where the hospital was located. I went to the personnel Office and asked if they were hiring, and they said yes.

After speaking with a clerk in the personnel office, she gave me an application, told me to take it home, and filled it out and return it the next day for an interview. When I came back the next day, I walked into the personnel office; they looked at my application, gave me a brief interview, and after finding it satisfactory, they hired me.

I completed the personnel paperwork, and I started to work immediately. That first day I work for Eight-hours from Eight O'clock in the morning until Five O'clock in the afternoon. My schedule was Eight hours a day, five days a week, with weekends off.

I began working as a Storeroom Clerk, earning $95.00 dollars a week, making deliveries of stationery supplies and hospital medical equipment throughout the hospital. After working there for several months, the Department Manager called me into his Office.

He praised me for the work I was doing and asked me if I would be interested in assuming the role of the supervisor for the section. I asked him, "What about the people you have working here already? What are they going to say when they find out that you hired me without giving them the opportunity for the position?

They have been here before me, and they are not going to like it. They are going to be upset and file a grievance with the labor union. This is going to cause a big mess, something I do not want to happen." He replied, "I'll worry about that when the time comes. Do you want the job, yes, or no?" "I said yes." For a man who had just returned from Vietnam and had no expectation of finding a job so quickly, I found myself extremely fortunate and blessed in finding a job with good working hours, a pleasant working environment and good people.

I was working for several months before I met my lovely

wife, who wanted nothing to do with me… Every time I saw her in the hallway while walking out of her office or to the cafeteria, I would try to get her attention with no success. She would always find a reason to avoid me.

One day during my morning coffee break, as I was going to the cafeteria with my Supervisor, I saw her going in the same direction with a girlfriend to the cafeteria. At that moment, I said to my supervisor, "You see that Girl, she is going to be my wife: He said to me, not in your life. She and her girlfriend are always surrounded by Doctors at the Cafeteria. I continued to walk behind her to the cafeteria.

With my persistence and goodwill, I was able to get close enough to talk to her friend and get to know her. All three of us sat together on the same coffee counter. I tried sitting next to her, but she was able to get her friend between us.

Not to make a big deal, I left it at that. I then had my coffee and Danish, and before walking out of the cafeteria, I offered to pay for her and her friends' breakfast, but she said, "No thanks, I have my own money, and I can pay for my own breakfast." I replied, "Okay, maybe the next time." She replied, "There isn't going to be the next time." After that, I said, "I'll see you later," she then replied, "Not if I can help it."

While walking out of the cafeteria, I said to myself, that woman is going to be my wife. As time progressed, we became friends. I would buy her flowers and take them to her Office where she worked. Eventually, she gave in and became my girlfriend. I would visit her every day at her office and take her to lunch with me. Other times she would come to where I was working, she would bring me coffee, and we would talk during her break.

This woman was the most beautiful woman I had ever seen. She was young, with long deep brown hair, a clear, clean complexion, and the most beautiful smile you could ever imagine. In addition, she has a body on her that looks like a brand new Classic Spanish guitar with all her string attached. She was nice from top to bottom, and there was no doubt about it… She was my top price reward from "God" for going to Vietnam and returning in one piece.

Most of the Doctors who knew her wanted to take her out. I found myself competing with other males for her affection and friendship. The rumors around the hospital were that could a person who just came back from Vietnam and could be suffering from post-traumatic stress disorder (PTSD) was lucky enough to be the one who would conquer her heart. This went on for several months before I started to take her home to the Bronx, where she lived.

After several months of going out, she first met my father

before she had the nerve to introduce me to her family. The day I introduced her to my father, he pulled me aside and said, "Son, she is a lovely young girl; take diligent care of her and be nice to her. Do not make the same mistake I made by not treating your mother the way she should have been treated. If I had treated her differently, had taken more time, showing her more love and affection as she deserved, your mother would still be here today."

That day, I said to my dad, "I am going to take my girlfriend home when I return. We are going to have a nice long talk, okay." He said, "Alright, just be careful taking her home because the Bronx is not like it used to be; the crime rate in that part of the city has gone up." "Don't worry, Dad, I know how to take care of myself;" "I know you do, Son, please just be careful, Okay," I then left.

The following day, both my father and I sat across from each other at the kitchen table where we could talk. That is when he started talking, and I began to listen. He began to open up and started telling me about all the problems he was having with his financial commitment that he had with other people. He told me about the bills, about the arguments; he had with my mother, which caused her to leave him.

I started talking to him to make him feel more comfortable with himself by building his self-esteem to have him open up and tell me all that had happened while I was away. After a while, he seemed solemn and quiet, not wanting to talk about his wife, my mother. I began trying to make him feel important by telling him how I felt about him and about all the good things he had taught me when I was a young child.

He told me how much he regretted not being the man she deserved, and she wanted him to be. He told me how he loved her very much and how he felt responsible for her leaving him because of his drinking and uncontrollable behavior. I then asked him, "You just said to me that you felt responsible for her leaving. Are you responsible?" That is when I noticed a change in his voice because he did not seem anxious to talk anymore.

He then got up from his chair and began walking away, saying to me, "Son, I do not feel well enough to continue this conversation, I am going to lie down for a while because I am not in the best of health, and at this moment I am not feeling well. I hope you understand," I replied, "No problem, Dad, I do understand, go ahead and lie down; we can always continue this conversation some other day when you are up to it, okay." I followed him to his room, making sure he got into bed; I then approached him, giving him a kiss on his forehead, telling him that I loved him while putting out the light as I was on my way out of the room, closing the door behind me.

After my father had gone to bed, I noticed some paperwork by the side of a desk; he had in the living room. As I looked through them, I noticed medical bills and other bills that had not been paid. I looked at the dates, and they were old. Some went as far back as the year; some were from collection companies. I began to put them in order so that I could add them up and get a total. After doing that for a while, the total came to four thousand dollars. He even had bills that he owed to the neighborhood (Bodega), a Grocery store that belonged to his friend.

While looking at the clock, I noticed that it was time to go to bed. I went to the front door to check that the door was closed and turned off all the lights as I walked to my room to go to bed.

The following day, I got up early and checked on my dad to make sure he was okay. Seeing that he was still sound asleep, I then walked out quietly, closing the door slowly behind me in order not to wake him up. I then went and took a quick shower, got dressed, went into the kitchen, and prepared myself breakfast. When I finished eating, I washed the utensil that I was using, cleaned the kitchen table, and walked over to the window.

While I was looking out, I could see the weather was getting nasty, and I could see dark clouds overhead, which meant rain was on its way. I took my jacket that I had brought from Vietnam, put it on and walked out the front door closing it behind me and locking it. I then rushed across the street, hoping that it would not start raining because I did not feel like being wet and walked as fast as I could about two blocks to the Grocery store. When I got there, I went in and asked to see the owner; a clerk told me that the owner had just left and that he would be back in a few hours. He then asked me if he could help me. I said, "No that I would return later," and I left.

It was the same store I used to work in part-time after school when I was in junior high school. Sweeping, mopping the floors, and packing the Refrigerators with beers and soda. Furthermore, where my father would stop by for a while to talk with his friend and have a few beers while coming from work on his way home.

I continued to walk the neighborhood for a few more hours afterward, returning to the Grocery store. As I went into the store, a large Hispanic white elderly male approached me, asking me if I had been in his store asking for him. I told him, "Yes," I then asked him, "Are you the new owner?" He said, "Yes," that he had bought the store from the previous owner two years ago.

He then asked me why I wanted to know that. I told him that I used to work part-time after school while in Junior High school for the previous owner. I then told him my reason for asking. "Do you have a customer who has a Son in Vietnam;" he replied, "Yes," He then asked me, "is my friend okay has something happened to him?" I said, "No, I'm his son, and I am here to pay some bills he owes you." He then said, "Listen, young man, your father does not owe me anything. He is the only one that pays his bills on time. That is why he always had good credit with me."

I told him the reason I came to see him was because I had found old grocery bills in a pile he had that needed to be paid, and they were from his store. He then said, "Your Father just forgot to get rid of them; we all do that sometimes.

How is your old man? Anyway, I have not seen him for weeks; I hope he is all right; tell him to drop by for beers just like old time's sake." I replied, "I will, and thank you for being a friend to my dad." He replied, "Don't mention it; your dad is a great person; I only wish they were all like him." I then left the store with a great deal of relief that some bills were paid. I just had to go and contact the rest of the people he owed money to and clear his dept. End.